1. This book may be kept three weeks. It is to be
   returned on / before the last date stamped below.
               ʰarged for every week or

SIX FOR HEAVEN

Theodora Montgomery was born in a mining town in the middle of the West Australian desert. From her Irish father, homesick for the shores of Liffey, she inherits his love of words which ring in her head like music. Having to leave their rectory home after his death, her mother buys a boarding house to provide a home and living for Theodora and her three sisters. We follow their lives from childhood to young womanhood with their friendships and loves, careers and marriages.

Books by Lucy Walker in the
Ulverscroft Large Print Series:

LUCY WALKER

Six for Heaven

Complete and Unabridged

ULVERSCROFT
Leicester

First published (as by Dorothy Lucie Sanders) 1952

First Large Print Edition
published July 1981
by arrangement with
Collins, London & Glasgow

To My Mother

British Library CIP Data

Walker, Lucy
    Six for heaven.—Large print ed.
    (Ulverscroft large print series: romance)
    I. Title
    823'.9'1F

    ISBN 0-7089-0650-8

Published by
F. A. Thorpe (Publishing) Ltd.
Anstey, Leicestershire

Printed and Bound in Great Britain by
T. J. Press (Padstow) Ltd., Padstow, Cornwall

AUTHOR'S NOTE

Though written in the first person, this story is not to be confused with autobiography. The story is fictitious and all the characters are imaginary.

For permission to include certain quotations from A. E. Housman's *A Shropshire Lad*, I am indebted to the Society of Authors as Literary Representatives of the Trustees of the Estate of the late A. E. Housman and Messrs. Jonathan Cape, Ltd., publishers of A. E. Housman's *Collected Poems*.

"I expect he thinks we're all hell-bent," Theodora said morosely.
"On the contrary, I think you're all six for heaven," said Sam.

Love is
a time of enchantment:
in it all days are fair and all fields
green. Youth is blest by it,
old age made benign: the eyes of love see
roses blooming in December,
and sunshine through rain. Verily
is the time of true-love
a time of enchantment—and
Oh! how eager is woman
to be bewitched!

Part One

Part One

1

I REMEMBER

1

I REMEMBER . . .! Not the house where I was born. That was a little dusty Rectory in Boulder City, which, for all its pretentious name, was no more than a shadeless, sand-blown, gold-mining town in the middle of the West Australian desert. My parents took me from that town when I was but three months old. We went west to the coast where my father had become Rector of Pepper Tree Bay.

In Pepper Tree Bay is the house I re-member.

It was brick, verandaed, and red-tiled. A row of pepper-corns and a picket fence stood between it and the Church. It had wide grounds at the back where vegetables, the pride of my father's heart, and fruit trees flourished. And where a cow was kept in one paddock and twenty or thirty fowls in

3

another. There was a big old red-gum on the grass plot outside the back door and another of giant size in the front of the house. They were beautiful trees. Old, massive, untidy, with gum-ridden pock marks down their great wide trunks. The shadows amongst the dark shining leaves were a world for the people of a child's fantasy, and the pungent odour of gum leaves, crushed and wet, filled the heart of that child with a delight that had no equal.

All round the house was a tangle of untidy buffalo grass.

The Church, mellowed with time—as we understand time in Australia—sat squat, buttressed in stone, on the corner of the high road that ran between Perth on the river and Fremantle on the shores of the Indian Ocean. It was shingle-roofed and ivy covered its walls. Two hundred yards to the south was the river and two miles to the west was the ocean.

At the time my parents took up the preferment there were only two children, myself and my elder sister Vicky who was so pretty that people passing in the street stopped to admire her shining head of curls and her small doll-like face.

4

All this I remember. But mostly I remember my father.

He was a big man with a thick thatch of black hair and deep blue eyes; he had classical features with a fine square forehead. He was the handsomest man in Pepper Tree Bay and he wore a wide plain gold ring on the little finger of his left hand. He banged his left hand down on the table when he was laying down the law, and the gold ring flashed. At the end of the dining-room in the Rectory was a great mahogany sideboard with a mirror, and when he wasn't laying down the law he would look up from the end of the table, turn his head a little sideways so he could see his reflection in the mirror, and brush his left hand over his hair. The gold ring always flashed.

When my father wanted to hail anyone—or silence them, or command an audience, which was often—he would hold out his hand with the palm turned upwards like a policeman on point duty, and the ring would flash like all the gold of Kalgoorlie.

Another important thing about my father was that he was a man who knew Hassie.

It seemed to us that to have known Hassie was a wonderful thing. When my mother had

5

offended my father, or when he was disappointed with something or angry about someone he always said . . . "Hassie would not have tolerated that . . . Hassie would not have said that to me."

Sometimes when he had drunk too much Irish whiskey he would tell us sadly that his life would have been different if only Hassie had been with us.

I don't think he ever told us, or even Mother, who Hassie really was. But we knew she was very beautiful, "the greatest of all Irish beauties." We knew that she sat a horse as no other woman in Ireland did; that she rode to hounds; that she won the point-to-point, whatever that was; that she had red-brown hair and a voice "that made the angels weep." We knew she was kind and gentle and that she played the *Invitation to the Waltz*.

We knew too that my father longed for the day when he would leave this land of sin, sorrow and sand; this land of vulgarians and barbarians and come again by the shores of the Liffey. And he always said that Hassie would be waiting for him.

Old Dr. Riley, who had been to school with my father in Dublin, said there wasn't any Hassie. That he made it all up. But even now

6

I can't bring myself to believe that Hassie had never even been born.

I remember my mother working and worrying. But I can't see her as I can see my father. I can see him coming down the passage and hear the heavy fall of his footsteps. I can see his feet sticking out of the end of his bed because he was so tall and he didn't like a covering on his feet, even in winter.

I can hear him in the Church as the words of Morning Prayer fell from his lips. I can hear him reading the Bible, I can see him ascending the pulpit and while he waited in the tiny silence before he began his sermon I can see him brush his hair with his left hand. I can see and hear him as he stood before the altar, raising his hand to pronounce the Benediction. His voice had the music of all Ireland in it, and when he pronounced those last words to a service it seemed to me to be a moment so profound, so beautiful as to be unearthly.

I can hear my father denouncing the countryside with all the caustic wit of the true exile. "Call that green!" he would cry, pointing his great stick towards the bushland. "'Tis grey, and a drear grey at that. Why, people in Australia have never seen green grass."

He would knock his stick against an old and crabbed banksia.

"God bless my soul," he would cry, his voice astounded. "Can this thing be called a tree? The Arabs would banish it from their presence."

Only the river pleased him. When it lay blue and shining, rimmed by gold and distant blue on a summer's day, he said nothing against it. But when the sky was overcast and the mists crept away from the shining distant reaches and the boats lay calm in the shadowed bay, he would relent.

"'Tis a lovely thing. People in the old country have never seen anything so calm, so peaceful; so fine in all degree. 'Tis surely a most lovely river."

Above everything else I can hear him declaiming poetry. There weren't any of the great epic or oratorical poems in English literature that my father did not know from memory. The words fell and flowed away from him like rivers of majestic beauty. The words rang in my head like a vast music.

Once when I was eight or nine years of age my father came home late for his lunch. He was always late. He was always injured and enraged by the fact that the meal was over,

8

perhaps by as much as a whole hour, and his portion had to be retrieved from the oven.

On this occasion he was left in lonely splendour at the head of the dining-room table where he ate his meal slowly and judiciously with long pauses in the eating to denounce the cruelty of his family in serving up such a meal, and piteously calling on the ghost of Hassie to witness his humiliation in this land of sorrow.

"Roll on, thou dark and deep blue ocean, roll," he declaimed. Looking up he saw me standing beside him, my wide eyes giving him all the audience he required in this mood.

"Ten thousand fleets sweep over thee in vain;
Man marks the earth with ruin—his control
Stops with the shore; upon the watery plain
The wrecks are all thy deed, nor doth remain
A shadow of man's ravage, save his own,
When for a moment, like a drop of rain,
He sinks into the depths with bubbling
    groan,
Without a grave, unknelled, uncoffined, and
    unknown."

It seemed to me, in my small and limited

world, there had suddenly poured into that shabby room an ecstasy of beauty.

"Who wrote it?" my father thundered.

"I don't know," I said, terrified of the consequence of my ignorance yet exalted by my first conscious knowledge of sensuous beauty.

"Lord Byron!" my father thundered. "'Twould make an angel shed tears of blood! A child of mine and she hasn't heard of Lord Byron! Shades of the dead and the great defend you. You're no child of mine. Get out of my sight, you ignoramus!"

I dodged his angry ring-gleaming hand and waited until he had taken himself off to his study. Then I hunted in the bookshelves until I found the green morocco-bound volume of Byron and I found these magic words. . . .

"Roll on, thou dark and deep blue ocean, roll. . . ."

The book went with me to bed and in the secret hours of the night and early morning I recited the first two stanzas again and again.

Within a day or two I had forgotten my father's rage and high up in the branches of the pepper tree was declaiming to the skies this new and lovely magic. From below I heard my father's voice.

"Get down from that tree and come here!"

10

I crawled down slowly.

"Where did you learn that?"

"Out of the green book in the book-case," I said nervously.

"And for what reason?"

Fear of my father prompted me to flatter him by saying that I had learned it to please him but some deeper honesty to poetry held me silent.

"Answer me," he roared. I hung my head and kicked the dust. Quick as lightning came that heavy, ringed hand across the side of my head. I dodged away beyond the pepper trees.

From that distance I defied him.

"Because I liked the words," I said.

Rage fell from him like a cloak falling to the ground.

"Come here, Doffy," he said softly.

I was wary. I took a step around the pepper tree but remained carefully out of range.

"So you liked the words, Doffy? They meant something to you?" I wasn't so frightened of him now. He had called me "Doffy". He did that only in moments of rare kindness and affection.

Suddenly he dug his hand in his trouser pockets and brought out a two-shilling piece.

"Here," he said. "Take this." He threw

the coin and I caught it. "I'm sorry I smacked you," he said gruffly.

It was the only time my father ever gave me a present, except a book of poetry he brought back from the war, and the only time he ever showed repentance for a blow struck or harsh words uttered.

2

Before the poetry incident, however, there came Mary, and after her Denney and Gerry.

I always held it against my mother that she told the tale of how she scrubbed out the Church in Boulder City the day before I was born. This story was intended to illustrate the harshness of the life of clergymen and their wives in the outbacks of Australia. Sometimes one dreams of the strangeness of a man like my father, fresh from the halls of learning and Trinity College, Dublin, coming to these remote fastnesses of the earth and of his first years in the deep bush at a tin-mining camp and later in Boulder City.

However, I never thought there was anything praiseworthy in the moral of this story of my mother's. I felt that it humbled the occasion of my expected arrival a trifle more than was necessary. It seemed that my mother made an unnecessary martyr of herself, for certainly my father martyred her enough without herself taking a hand in the business. It didn't seem to me that scrubbing Church floors added anything to my prestige . . . and God knows I needed it enough. I was a plain child, and from what history relates a bad-tempered one.

My father tyrannised over my mother in the matters of parish service. He sent her hither and thither at any hour of the day and night. He was completely without any understanding of the difficulties of running a home with immature and cheap servants. My mother had been a nurse before her marriage and whenever my father found the sick poor amongst his parishioners he dispatched her forthwith to give of her services. The nurse-girl would carry the burden of the home inadequately. My mother, weary and at her wits' end, would return to a house resounding with disorder and a disgruntled Irishman who would demand of the shades of the dead and the great why he should thus be treated to a potential lifetime of domestic chaos.

My mother's patients in the parish were without number. Babies died easily in those days. Bad drains, plagues of flies, ignorance in treating fevers, diabolical summers kept the infantile mortality high.

Nor were these all the demands upon my mother.

My father was an indefatigable labourer in the causes of Church Schools, Friendly Societies, Mothers' Unions, Parish Choir Clubs. He had a genius for organising and inspiring service. But it was Mother who was sent forth to the weekly meeting to keep the band together.

As the years crept on the Rectory grew more shabby, the undisciplined children more rowdy; my mother though more worn and weary still keeping her soft skin with its quick flush, the blue brightness of her eyes. And the handsomeness of my father made my heart swell with pride. I envied and admired his arrogance; unconsciously I imitated the way he would lift his left hand in a commanding attitude so that he called me the Sergeant-Major. Mother, more practical, decided that I should become a school-teacher.

In the weeks before Mary's birth a dreadful epidemic of typhoid fever raged in the gold-fields. Inevitably the disease spread to the coast but was never as widespread or as virulent as the goldfields plague.

One day my father, home from visiting in the parish, came stamping and shouting through the house for Mother. She came to the kitchen door wiping her floury hands on her apron.

"Whatever's all the noise about, Joe?" she said in exasperation. "Why must you shout at me?"

"The Billings," he said. "They've got some fever. Old Jack, Mrs. Billings and one of the girls. The other children can't manage. You'll have to have them here. Or better still, go down and see what you can do for them in their own house."

My mother went down to the Billings' and did not come home for three months.

She knew at once that old Mr. Jack had typhoid and that the other two patients were probably in the first stages. She sent for Dr. Riley. Between them they discovered the Billings had no money to pay for a nurse and hospitalisation was impossible and not compulsory in those days. My mother spoke to my father on the telephone.

"They've got typhoid fever and hardly any money," she said.

"Then stop there and look after them," he commanded.

"But Joe, it's typhoid! I'm not thinking of myself. It's the children. Vicky and Theodora and the new baby . . . it's not even born."

"We can look after ourselves up here," he said blithely. "You'll have to stay in quarantine with the Billings. The new baby won't hurt. Tim Riley says the unborn child is immunised."

So Mother stayed. She nursed night and day, did all the housework and cooking. All the family survived, my mother did not get the disease, and she came home in time to make herself a cup of tea and brush her hair before the first pains heralded Mary's imminent arrival.

The Billings were eternally grateful to my mother. They thought she was an angel. But they thought my father was an Inspired Angel and one who stands on the Right Hand.

2

THE SCHOOL

1

ONE morning in the mid-summer of 1912 there came to the Rectory a Mr. Greenwood and with him his two boys. Mr. Greenwood was a prosperous wool-grower and he had brought his sons to Perth to have them tutored.

"What brings you on my doorstep?" my father asked with pretended surprise. His friends had already told him that Mr. Greenwood was coming to Perth to see him about the boys.

"You prepared that Butler boy for the Naval College," Mr. Greenwood said bluntly. "What about my boys? I want you to take 'em on."

"Ah now," said my father in his most dulcet tones. "That would be asking something indeed!"

"They've no schooling where they are."

17

Landowners in those prosperous days were accustomed to stating a case and not asking for anything. Also Mr. Greenwood, I have no doubt, could sum up an impulsive Irishman as well as he could a mob of sheep.

"Ah! And the fine boys they are!" my father said softly.

"The nearest school's a State school and it's eight miles away. Schools in Perth are full up." Mr. Greenwood stopped short a minute. "They're no good anyway," he said loudly.

"Ah, now, that's a bad thing," said my father. "That's a bad thing indeed." He made no mention of the fact that he hated coaching. He loathed inky stupid boys when they were inky and stupid though boys in their leisure hours had a strong appeal for him.

"You'll take 'em on?"

"And where would they be fed? And who would be looking after them?"

"You've got a big place here. I'll make it worth your while." Mr. Greenwood was bargaining as if hiring out a string of ponies for foddering. In an oblique way, however, this was a good move, for in money matters my father was full of pride. His voice now was sorrowful.

18

"I'm a minister of God not of Mammon, Mr. Greenwood. You can leave the boys here by all means but I'll be thanking you to make out any cheque you have in mind to the Church Council."

My mother in the kitchen wrung her hands.

"Isn't that your father all over? Take from his own children to give to others! Does he think the housekeeping money will stretch to feed two more?"

It was typical of her that she did not see the madness, only the absurd generosity, in his gesture. She responded to the demand on a minister of religion with the same sense of mission as my father did, but she was angry that he did not accept from Mr. Greenwood enough money to feed the boys.

Part of the veranda was partitioned off and the boys installed the following week.

For the first few days lessons began punctually at nine and proceeded until eleven. After midday the boys were supposed to give themselves up to the digesting and learning of poetry while my father had his siesta and then went about his parish.

In the second week the Greenwoods' three male cousins arrived.

19

"Joe, for pity's sake have reason! How are we to feed them?" For once my father saw her point of view. He was tired of the noise and tired of asking for marmalade to be passed to find it had been emptied by the eldest Greenwood in passing.

"They're eating us out of house and home! They've the manners of bog Irish!" he cried. "Here am I, no more than a poverty-stricken Irishman! Yet I can do more about schooling children in this God-forsaken country than the Church Council. What a country! Nincompoops, idiots, ignoramuses!"

"You must let the Greenwoods pay us for the children and we'll get another house," said my mother.

He brushed her aside with a wave of his hand. He stood up and went into the passage where he began to put on his great pith helmet and gather up his sticks and books.

"I'll show them what Joe Montgomery can do," he said. "Here am I . . . a man without a boy, a brick, or a penny . . . but a Church School we'll have before I'm a day older."

At two o'clock he returned with the title-deeds of a twenty-acre block of land on a river frontage and five hundred pounds in his pocket.

My mother flew into action. Within twenty-four hours a big house on the river-front had been rented, advertisements for domestic staff had been inserted in the daily paper.

Within a fortnight we had moved to the great house on the river-banks and only two hundred yards down the road from the Church. With the rapidity of a miracle two wooden schoolrooms were built and a school had been created.

It had a mushroom growth.

Tutors were unprocurable in the fastnesses of the West Australian Nor'-West, and furthermore my father's erudition and gift of the golden tongue were already legendary in the wilderness. When he had first come from Ireland he had lived in the North and had travelled as far as horseman could go to the outlying farms and stations. He was well known and befriended by many of the families of old pioneers, so that word he had started a school spread through their ranks like a bush fire. My father had a peculiar charm for them. To their barren and often calloused minds he brought the whiff of cultural learning.

In the Squatters' Clubs, in the drawing-rooms of their town houses, in the cabins of their big river launches he provided wondrous and scintillating conversation. Men who had watched thousands of sheep or cattle die in a drought; who had killed a spearing black out of hand, who had watched floods destroy their homesteads; who had stood single-handed, and of necessity *on foot,** against stampeding mobs of frenzied cattle smelling water, sat like chastened children and listened to my father as he dispensed of English lore and Irish wit.

So their children came scuttling to his school.

Except for discourses, very brilliant and witty on English literature and, more occasionally, on Latin translations, my father loathed school-teaching. He had two curates now and both found it was they who took over the chief burden of discipline and of routine teaching whilst my father went about the parish boasting of his school, roping in new boys and prising large sums of money from the Squattocracy.

*Stampeding cattle can only be stopped by man or men *on foot*. They are afraid of man on foot, but not of men on horseback. It requires iron nerve but has to be done.

22

My mother was Matron, Nurse and General Organiser.

Occasionally, when the staff failed, she surreptitiously cooked, washed and cleaned.

My father's idea of discipline was certainly ruthless if not consistent.

The school had been established a period of two years when World War broke out. At the time there were three German boys amongst the pupils. Two of them were brothers and their father was a wealthy and well-bred German shipping agent. The third boy was the son of a banker who had himself been born in South Australia of German parents. The two brothers, Hans and Willi Schmidt, were boarders. On the day war was declared their father, in the interests of the German shipping firm he represented, wirelessed to sea to warn his ships. Schmidt was immediately arrested on the charge of sending military intelligence to the enemy. He was likely to be interned for the duration of the war.

"I'll keep the boys here," my father announced.

Just before nine o'clock lessons next morning a large commotion behind the schoolrooms called attention to itself and my father stamped off in that direction.

The entire school stood in a half-ring around three sapling gum trees that were backed by the high school fence. The Schmidt boys and Frank Deschen were tied to the three trees. Six of the senior boys were armed with stones and the three German boys were literally being stoned.

My father's voice thundered through the crowd. Within five seconds the semicircle had been transfixed in fear by that terrible voice. He unroped the three boys and sent them with one of the masters up to my mother. With a few giant strides my father had gone into the school, armed himself with a cane, leapt over the low balcony to the playground and stood in a cold anger before the school. Boys under ten were sent off with the curate and the rest of the semicircle was ordered to close ranks.

"There is only one way to treat cowards," my father said. He caned the whole school.

2

By this time there had come Mary and Denney and Gerry. Five girls.

"Shades of the dead and the great!" my father would cry. "What have I done that I should be cursed by so many women. Out of my sight!" he would cry. "Or it's the back of both my hands for the lot of you."

One day a man came from Ireland who had been at Trinity with my father. I had to carry in the tray with the bottle of Irish whiskey and the glasses.

"This is my second daughter, Theodora," my father said. The man, a Mr. Hanrahan from County Meath, gave a rich laugh.

"And what are you laughing at?" said my father faintly belligerent. The man, tall and military, stared at me and I was conscious of my shabby dress.

"Just like you, Joe," said Mr. Hanrahan, "to give the child a name like that. Theodora! God bless me! What a mouthful. . . . Theodora Montgomery! What made you think of it?"

I thought he must have known my father very well in Ireland to be able to laugh at him in Australia. My father could not tolerate laughter or criticism.

"The gift of God," said my father theatrically. "Theodora! The gift of God!" He turned and went to the door.

25

"Helen," he roared. "Bring in the rest of them. I want the children, all of them."

My mother came hastily to the study door. "Why, Joe," she said protesting. "They're not dressed for company."

"Bring them in," said my father. "Bring in the whole gaggle of 'em. Now then you two, get over by the wall." For Vicky had come with my mother clinging to and hiding behind her skirts. That was the way Vicky always moved about.

Presently Mary came slowly into the room holding Denney by the hand and then my mother came carrying Geraldine.

"Line up," said my father. "Number off from the right!"

We stood self-consciously by the wall, all except the baby. Mother had sat her on a cushion. My father gestured to us one at a time.

"Victoria Yvonne Montgomery; Theodora Eileen Montgomery; Mary Cathleen Montgomery; Denille Shannon Montgomery; Geraldine Rory Montgomery."

He was speaking our names with pride and bravado, his voice making such a mellifluous music of them all that I was never again ashamed of them. He turned to his friend, the man from Ireland. Mr. Hanrahan was smiling.

"There's the sound of Ireland in them, Joe," he said. "But it's a strange land to be hearing the waters of the Shannon in the names of a gaggle of girls."

"Och, it's a terrible land," said my father turning from us, no longer interested in his female progeny. "'Tis a land of sorrow," said my father. "Of terrible sin and wickedness.

"'Tis full of such a vice and wickedness you wouldn't know about, William. 'Tis a dry, cruel country and fit only for blackfellows."

Thus my father spoke of Australia.

He poured out the Irish whiskey and with one wave of his hand dismissed us from his presence.

Outside the study window, which was always left open a few inches at the bottom, I could sit on the edge of the veranda and while looking up lovingly into the old gum tree could listen to everything my father said about Ireland.

Mr. Hanrahan came often to the house and because he was newly come from Ireland, my father's friends, who had known Mr. Hanrahan in the old country, came often to see him. There was Dr. Riley and Mr. Thompson, a solicitor; and Father Byrne, the Roman Catholic priest who lived on the hill near his Church; and Mr. Holland, a retired bachelor gentleman who lived in a big house around the river. They would fill up the small study to overflowing. The leather chairs and the leather couch were replete with them. They would drink Irish whiskey and tell lies to one another about Ireland.

"You remember Tom Flanagan? It's in my mind to tell you about the day his brother brought the blood mare to Crossakeil. . . ."

And after a while, when the story was at the point of greatest excitement, one of my father's friends would say . . .

"There's not a word of truth in what you're saying. Now I had it from Rory Moore who was himself there on the day. . . ."

Then another of them, perhaps Tim Riley, would take up the thread of a tale and presently a great hand would slap down on the leather arm of the chair and a great voice be lifted. . . .

"That's a damned lie, Riley. Indeed and it is. I was there on the day myself and Colonel O'Brien had been dead and in his grave ten years. . . ."

When the whiskey had mellowed the moods of my father and his friends I could tell that besides all these stories there also came out of Ireland the saddest of all tears . . . the tears of men who were nostalgic for their own land.

3

TO THE WARS—AND BACK

1

PRESENTLY my father went to the war.

He had been around the military camps giving talks to the soldiers and conducting services. The men would do anything for him. It was not only the power of the tongue and his almost absurd generosity that held them but a deeper knowledge and understanding he had of the psychological needs of men going from their homes, crossing vast tracts of ocean, and contemplating the possibilities of violent death.

My father never talked down to the men. He could order them around and would not suffer his own opinions to be disputed, but beneath all his arrogance there was an awareness of the other man's right to live and right to have his own place in the social life of his country.

Thus it was, late in 1915, a new headmaster was installed in the school, we removed back to the Rectory and my father appeared in uniform.

I can see now the day he went to the war. In the morning he went into the school to say good-bye to the boys. He came striding out of the double gates with the boys streaming after him. He stepped into a car which moved slowly down Perth-Fremantle Road with the boys still swarming. Never was there such an escort. People on the pathways stopped and gazed in amazement as the schoolboys streamed past on every kind of vehicle and many of them still on foot.

There began three hard years for those left behind.

We were back in the Rectory but without servants. We had my father's aggression and emotional instability but we had Mother's will to work. I don't say we worked well or with quiet efficiency. Far from it. We quarrelled, with the probable exception of Mary, relentlessly.

Vicky, who had a doll-like prettiness, wept easily and my mother always protected her. Though I was younger, I was bigger and had an explosive temper. Perhaps I resented

Vicky's sheltering. Mary was a gentle and attractive child and I bossed her around unnecessarily. Denney and Gerry were still little more than babies; naughty and wilful.

I remember my Waterloo with Mary.

If she was told to do a thing she did it at once and with beautiful execution. We all slept on the side veranda of the Rectory. We were allowed to read in bed at night, and when I was ready for sleep I used to command Vicky or Mary to get out of bed and turn off the light. It was Mary's turn.

"Get out and turn off the light, Mary," I said.

"Turn it off yourself," came the wholly unexpected answer.

"You get out and turn it off," I commanded, horrified at this first rebellion.

"I won't."

"I'll tell Mother."

"Tell her then. I won't turn it off."

Instinct told me that if Mother was called she would see the justice of my taking a turn and I would be humiliated before the others. I was confronted with the awful problem of MAKING Mary turn off the light. Physically it was impossible. It was clearly a battle of wills.

"Then I shan't," I said. "I'm going to sleep and you can leave it on. When Mother comes out she'll thrash you."

"No, she won't," said Mary. "Vicky's got a cold so she won't blame her. You're the next eldest so she'll blame you."

This was sound and dreadful logic. My mother's abiding fault in disciplining her children was always to put the onus of fault on the eldest present.

It was me, Theodora, who always collected the "You're the eldest" talk.

We lay in bed for a long time. I listened fearfully for my mother's irate footstep and I listened hopefully for the creak of Mary's bed.

Time drifted on and I nearly fell asleep. My mother had clearly forgotten us, but what about when she came to bed? She also slept on the veranda.

I crawled out of bed and tip-toed to Mary's side. She was sound asleep.

There was nothing for it but to turn off the light. Mary had beaten me with a lash no stronger than the gentle rhythmical stroke of her breathing.

The turning off of the light was a testing-point. Mary knew I could never again MAKE

33

her do anything. She was amazingly just for a child. If I tried to bully her into doing anything again she would weigh and consider whether my demands had justice behind them. If so, she would get up and perform her duty with an appearance of indifference. If not, she flatly said so, and that was that.

There were two years between our ages and Mary and I rarely quarrelled. It was with Denney, who was four years younger than myself, that I was constantly at war.

The war years were hard for my mother. She had five contentious egoists to manage and try to train. She had all the work of the home and still a heavy burden of parish duties. Though her husband was away at the war she was still a leading figure in the Mothers' Union, the Girls' Friendly Society, the working bees for the Red Cross, for Soldiers' Widows and Children, for the Parish Poor. If her spirits wilted and there were times when her enthusiasm flagged my father's unseen spirit goaded her on. Thirteen thousand miles away he remained the taskmaster.

She never contemplated rebellion, for his command over her was a subtle one. It was not one of comrades-in-arms nor one of their shared wish for the good of the community. It was because in all their married years he had conveyed to her the insistence of his own superiority. Negatively he suggested her inferiority. He always *assumed* there would be incompetence on her part. Had she been a wiser and less sensitive woman she would have allowed her past and her deeds to speak for themselves. But subconsciously she was driven by the whiplash of his scorn.

My father was an Irishman with all the inconsistencies of the Irish temperament. No man had nobler aspirations or more tender cares for the halt and the blind and the lame of life. Yet he could not suffer frustration. No man can have all his own way all the time in life and when everything was not as he would wish it, like the whole race of Irish, he would abandon logic and justice and find the nearest scapegoat to hand.

And basically my father despised the Australian way of life. He was a product of Irish public schools and Trinity College, Dublin. His life in Ireland had been gentle, academic and his friends had been polished, erudite, correct.

The good in him, and the will to serve, had sent him forth to the antipodes where he found an ignorant race, aggressive by virtue of the stupendous fact that they had wrung not only a living but wealth from the nearest thing to a God-forsaken desert that he could imagine. When my father came to Australia at the turn of the century he found a race of people who had achieved the almost impossible. You couldn't tell THEM anything. And that was just my father's fault. He liked to tell people. He tried to bring the Irish, or English, way of living to their notice. He could not condemn their achievements, but he thundered against their coarseness, their ignorance in the things pertaining to the mind. He called them a race of vulgarians and barbarians, but he bowed before their bravery and endurance in their mastery over the land.

My mother was a colonial and her parents of North of England stock. She was amused and often entertained by the Irish temperament but she had no basic understanding of it. She had the colonist's ability for sheer graft and the North of Englander's rigid attitude to right and wrong. She had preconceived attitudes to the habits and behaviour of a minister of religion and she could never quite adapt herself to the unconventional. She had some kind of a conception of her own as to the kind of figure my father, as a minister of religion, should cut before the public. So in some ways she tried to make him over. Without even the beginnings of success, of course, in a man like my father. In fact he took the weapon out of her hand and tried to make her over.

She smoothed over harsh words he threw, in moments of temper, to his offending parishioners; she laboured his good points in public and boasted gently of his achievements.

Her reward was mostly the whip-lash of his scorn. When he had gentler or more tender moments she never recognised them until too late. His scorn lacerated her and she could not see or feel beyond her injuries.

In the war years she nearly worked herself to death trying to earn his good will. A forgiveness and an understanding and a philosophical attitude to all his Irish faults might have earned a better reward. She would have had to have been of the breed of angels, I suppose.

Between us we did the garden, the cow and the fowls; chopped and brought in wood from the vacant lots, scoured the house and cooked meals, washed up . . . and quarrelled vociferously.

My mother did all the washing. I can see her now bending over the tubs with soap suds up to her armpits and feel again the burning sense of shame and indignity to see her thus employed. We children hung out the clothes, pegged up, damped down and ironed. Oh yes, we knew how to work.

The only thing we couldn't or wouldn't do was plain sewing. And here my mother also balked. So we went about like a lot of rag-tags. We children didn't care, but my mother burned with shame at our torn clothes and grubby legs and tattered sandals. In the end she bought an iron-last and taught the three eldest to sole our own shoes and boots. We did it with remarkable and proud efficiency and the money saved paid an occasional seamstress to come in and mend our clothes.

When the war was over my mother had the vast sum of £250 in the bank.

4

THE BASTONS

WHEN my father came down the gang-plank of the hospital ship that brought him home from the war, I think I intuitively knew that our days in Pepper Tree Bay were numbered.

I was twelve years old, too immature to understand the difference in him; far too young to have had that foreboding of disaster.

I was aware of an acute sense of disappointment. The handsome hero with the raven black hair was gone. A middle-aged man with white hair, too portly to be healthy, came amongst us. I was aware too of a sense of shock and fear in my mother. I remember that I was desperately anxious she should cover it up. I was desperately angry with her because I knew she failed. Perhaps he too had a sense of disappointment. He too perhaps found the prettiness had faded from my mother's face and that her hands were calloused with too much hard work.

It was not only in appearances that he was a changed man.

His manner with other people had always been that of arrogance, tinctured with an Irish charm and inoculated with an Irish brogue. Now he was quiet, tired.

When my mother asked him about Ireland he replied wearily, "Ireland! Och, the dirty place! As for the Irish? They should shoot 'em all."

"Did you see Hassie?" I asked.

He did not even look at me. He stared out of the window of the car.

"Hassie's dead," he said. He was silent. "They're all dead. Dead and gone! 'Tis a sad and sorry land. Let's hear no more of it.

"Shoot 'em all," he said again, abruptly. "'Tis the only way to treat 'em. Wipe 'em off the face of the earth! Have done with 'em."

He did not speak of Ireland again. He never told anyone what happened to him in Ireland, but my mother thinks it was just disappointment. All the years he had been in Australia he had been nostalgic for Ireland and he had woven dreams in his mind of "going home." In 1918 he found Ireland sickening under the yoke of England's economic punishment. It was a poor place, and he knew it.

Yes, he came back to the Rectory a tired and disillusioned man; to five children who were strangers to him. His health was shaken and his spirit crippled.

The two and a half years that followed were strange years. They held many good times, even great times. Life was full of bustle and optimism, yet deep down there was a knowledge that there was a period to the artificial gaiety, a nemesis awaiting.

Amongst my father's friends was old Richard Baston. He was one of the last of the great original pioneers.

His favourite way of proving a political argument, and he was addicted to political arguments, was to rip off his coat and shirt and display the hideous scars made in his youth by blackfellows' spears.

"Don't tell me how to run this country!" he would cry. "Look at that! Blackfellows! Niggers! Fires, droughts, floods! I've beaten 'em all . . . and made it pay dividends. Don't tell *me* how to run this country!"

We children kept a respectable distance from Old Richard. We were afraid of his wild voice though fascinated by his history of courage and endurance. If one of us, or one of

41

his own sons or daughters, did something that displeased him he would shout.

"Up in the North, I'd shoot a nigger for less than that."

The daughters of the Baston family had been born and reared on the station in the North-west. What smattering of schooling they had received had been from half-baked governesses. They could read, paint a little on china, and tinker with the piano. There all semblance of culture ceased. Their girlhood had been spent the hard way amongst black-fellows and stockmen in the harsh climates of the inland. The two sons had had some schooling in Perth, but much of the veneer had worn off by the time they had returned for a year or two into the North. Yet these sons, whom a kinder fate might have made millionaires in their own land, were destined to end their lives as part of Australia's volunteer army in the mud of Flanders, fighting for a country they had never seen and for a cause they had never understood . . . yet fighting because it was a young man's prerogative to fight for England and the Empire.

The friendship between the Bastons and us Montgomerys developed because the Bastons

42

were ardent Church-goers. Moreover they were hospitable to the point of lavishness to those they liked. For those who had earned their displeasure their tongues were wicked whip-lashes, edged with the vocabulary of the North-west.

Vicky, Mary and I would go down to Innanup for our usual Sunday afternoon call. We loved this weekly visit not only because of the pink-iced walnut cake, the five-pound box of chocolates that was always open on the dining-room sideboard, the occasional launch trips or car rides but because there was something exciting and lovable as well as hard and intimidating about all the Bastons. We were allowed to roam all over the fine old house, play the gramophone and, best of all, listen to Anne, Margaret and Susan mimicking those of their friends and relations they disliked.

Old Richard was always dozing in the great arm-chair on the veranda.

"Hello, Vicky, m'dear," he would bellow. He would ignore Mary and me for it was Vicky he adored. "Come and sit on Papa Baston's knee."

Vicky, who was frightened of her own father, would clamber happily on the knee of the Terror of the North-west. It was more than his own children had ever done. Vicky would nestle her head against his hard wicked old breast as he would brush his fingers through her curly hair and presently present her with two half-crowns. He would have made one of his own sons plough an acre paddock before he would give him threepence to go to the swimming-baths on the river.

Mary and I would fade into the girls' quarters.

"Well, you kids here again!" Susan would exclaim affably.

"After the chocolates, I expect." This would be from Margaret. Yet if we missed a Sunday we would have been roundly called to account when next a Baston was encountered.

First would be the solemn rite of taking Mrs. Baston's tea to her. She was a white-haired lady of great gentleness and dignity who rarely left her private drawing-room. Looking at her lace-bedecked frailty no one would ever dream she had been one of the first white women in the North-west; that she had travelled alone, but for her young husband, through primeval bush and desert where no white man had set foot or ever been heard of. To us Montgomery children she had one unfailing idiosyncrasy far more enthralling than her exploits with blackfellows in the North. She had Reckitt's blue put in the rinse water when she had her hair washed.

When the afternoon tea rites were over we would give ourselves up to delivering the parish news. We knew, even at this early age, the interest the Baston girls took in gossip, and we listened eagerly to all our parents' conversations with the express purpose of entertaining the Bastons on Sunday afternoons. After we had delivered our bulletins would come the great moment when we heard ourselves the news of their world . . . the wondrous, scintillating grown-up social world.

"Uncle Rob's this year's President of the Racing Club. We're going to the Cup in the Governor's Box. Papa says we're to take Vicky as a mascot."

We clapped our hands in awe and glee.

"What shall you wear, Susan?"

"Margaret's just got a new race frock."

"What about Vicky? Mama says we're all tatterdemalions and she's ashamed of us. Vicky can't go in one of *our* old frocks."

"Don't worry," said Anne airily. "Miss Stetson is to make all the Bastons' frocks for Cup week, including Vicky's."

45

"The Regan-Calledons are going to give a big Race Ball."

"I doubt if we'll go," said Anne haughtily. "They only put the hyphen in their name *after* they came to this country."

"But Anne," I said. "They're descended from the Earl of Calledon."

"There was only one Earl of Calledon and he, my dear, was a bachelor."

"And, Anne, Regan-Calledon's father . . ." Margaret caught her sister's eyes and stopped. Curiously enough, they did not hesitate to say what was untrue and had a slightly immoral implication, yet they hesitated to pass on what was fact: namely, that Mrs. Regan-Calledon's father had been a bonded man, a political convict sent out from Ireland in the 1870s. The pioneering landowners had a sense of loyalty to one another, but it was a curious one.

Vicky spent most of her time with the Bastons. She would go and spend a Sunday afternoon and stay a week. Because of the impact of their personality and their way of living she became, in due course, more Baston than Montgomery. She had less of the Irish plausibility and more of the Baston hauteur. Because this manner in Vicky was no more

46

than a veneer, it was never very effective.

The post-war years were full of a lavish kind of splendour that poured from the too heavy purses of the pastoralists who lived in their town houses along the river-bank. Theirs was the life that was the key-note of our own social life in the aftermath of the war.

The two Baston nephews who were to inherit Innanup Station and, later, Anne, married. The weddings were events to be remembered in the annals of social history. Relatives and friends of the pioneering families came from all over Australia. The best hotels and clubs of Perth were set to catering. Musicians were employed, great marquees set up on the lawns of Innanup, vast quantities of rich and glamorous foods as well as floods of wines and beverages poured into the backway entrances to the home. Armies of servants and gardeners, chauffeurs, coachmen, nurse-girls were employed.

My father officiated at the weddings and at each Vicky was chosen as a bridesmaid because Papa Baston would have none other.

The weddings were followed by launch trips, garden parties, huge church bazaars, invitations to Government House where we

47

children played croquet and ate strawberries and cream from Doulton plates, and our parents wore splendid clothes and most of the men sported top-hats and morning suits.

There was another side of our lives too.

Vicky and I were old enough to ogle and be ogled by the choir-boys and the boys from Father's school. We went to nice sedate school dances before each one of which we had tearful rages with our mother to let us wear stockings. But in spite of bared knees and the recurring white dresses with insertion and torchon lace, the boys liked us, and we liked the boys.

In spite of all the wonders of this life there was an undercurrent of impending tragedy. My father was not the man he had been. He was constantly erratic and irascible. He was never witty or entertaining. His face was grey and his thickening girth was not the ordinary approaches of middle-age. His gait was closer and he was a prey to rheumatism. Every influenza epidemic caught my father first amongst its victims. He would be ill longer than anyone else and emerge from each attack looking greyer, older, and with a racking cough. He didn't go around the Parish so much; he called on the curate to take services more often than he would have dreamed of in earlier days.

In our own home fear stalked. We were hard-up for money and we were all at the educable age. Where were now my father's ideals of a classical education for his children? Where were his cries for higher and more cultural standards? He was content to send us to the State school and washed his hands of the responsibility of our education. He had come back from the war and found us a rough, quarrelsome crowd. Every time we opened our mouths we emitted the nasal drawl of the Australian accent. He didn't think we were material worth troubling about.

Mother thought differently. Out of her slender housekeeping she found the fees for Vicky at a private school. For me she sold a block of land and sent me to a Church of England Sisterhood. Mary had to win a scholarship for herself and earn her own secondary school education. Denney and Gerry were still very young and a year or two at the State school would give them a good grounding.

Meantime, day by day, my father's footsteps grew slower and more erratic. His head bowed and he ceased all parish visiting. My mother's face was troubled. There was fear in her eyes and I believe I was the only one of the children who saw it. Though we knew the foundations of our home and our security were rocking we children were never really afraid. My mother was a rock that no storms or tempests could weather away. Whatever happened to our father, to our livelihood, to our home . . . we had nothing to fear. We had our mother.

On a June night in 1921 my mother retired early to bed. She was worn out with a day's hard work. It seemed very late to me when I felt her hand gently shaking the bed-clothes.

"Doffy," she said. "Come inside with me. Come and get in my bed."

It was the only time in the whole of my life my mother used my nickname.

I was wide awake at once and scrambled out of bed. The big double bed that mother sometimes used in the front room was warm and cosy.

"What's the matter, Mama?"

She began to cry. A quiet pathetic endless kind of crying it was. It didn't frighten me though it shocked me. I felt important and thrilled to be the one called upon to share her worry.

"He'll come home," I said with the blind irrational faith of the child.

We lay for a long time, both wide awake, both silent. We listened to all the night sounds. Then quietly we heard it a long, long way away. A slow shuffling step that sometimes stopped and then came on erratic, painful, utterly tired.

We lay, frozen with anguish, and listened to it as it came nearer. I don't know why we did not move nor go to the assistance of that walker in the night. Partly we were stilled by the awfulness of the knowledge that was inherent in that step, partly by the deep abiding instinct that told us that our father as he walked down that dark shadowy street was utterly alone—and wished only to be alone. None of us had ever really touched him in his heart.

We lay there with the hand of dread upon us, with a kind of ultimate understanding of the loneliness of my father in this strange land.

It came on, louder—the tapping of a heavy stick, the failing footstep.

At last my mother sprang out of bed and switched on the lights.

The steps came up the drive, paused on the

stone steps of the porch. And then my mother, galvanised into action, opened the front door.

"Joe!" she whispered. "Joe!"

Even in this catastrophic moment she remembered the four sleeping children and she whispered to spare them. She whispered with the desperation of a woman who knows that the foundations of life are now rocking beneath her children's feet.

He said nothing but came on into the light of the hall. He leaned heavily on the door, then heavily on my mother. She helped him into the old leather chair in the study and he sat there breathing heavily, his eyes faded, full of tears, his face the face of an old, old man.

"It is the end, Helen," he said. "Ring up the Bishop."

"Joe?" my mother said pitifully. His hands were lying on the arms of the chair, the walking stick had fallen to the ground, the gold ring shone yellow in the electric light. He lifted his left hand then let it fall back. His head sunk on his chest.

Mother suddenly turned to me.

"Get hot-water bottles," she said. "Fix his bed."

Resolute she went to the phone and rang Dr. Riley. Together we pushed, dragged, lifted him to his bed. Mother undressed him and when Dr. Riley came striding through the open door unannounced, he was lying on his pillows, his breathing heavy, his eyes closed. He heard Dr. Riley's voice and his eyelids wavered open.

"'Twas not thus, Tim," he said, "that the kings of Ireland died." Then he said nothing as the doctor opened his pyjama coat.

"Ah Brian Borhu!" he said presently.

Those were the last words I remember hearing my father speak.

My mother did not have many moments of sound intuition in her life, but she had one now. Instinctively she knew it was Tim Riley, and Tim Riley alone, my father needed. Together they had known the cross at Kells, the wide fields of Crossakeil, the fork in the street outside Trinity, Burke's name engraved in the panelling of my father's study.

My mother turned and taking my hand went into the dining-room, we could hear their voices, soft and tender, loving as the night air in summer.

After a long, long time Dr. Riley came back

into the dining-room. He was folding his stethoscope.

"You are right, Helen," he said gently. "It is the end."

He sat down heavily and stared into the coals of the fire. My mother's face was white and pitiful. It was cold, like stone. Then Dr. Riley looked up and leaning over took her hand.

"Do not be too hard a judge," he said. "There was a bird in his breast. It fluttered and beat against the imprisoning body. It was a bird, like a lark, that would have risen straight to heaven with as pure a song, if it had found release. There was no release, and in the end it was the bird . . . the beating of its wings, the driving of its beak . . . that bled his heart to death."

Long afterwards when I stood on the steps of Dublin Post Office and saw the statue of the "Myth Boy" with the drooping head and the bird on his shoulder, I understood what Dr. Riley had meant. My father's story was the story of all Ireland, a wild imprisoned singing in the heart, and like the bird of the forest, it preys upon the host that feeds it.

5

TOM JONES

WHEN we were very young it was Vicky who was invited to the parties, and Vicky who had the party dresses.

Because we were comparatively poor and yet had to keep up with the social position of high rank in the Church of England, Mother had occasionally to give a children's party, and it was always a combined party. There couldn't be one for each of us.

"The children of the Rev. Dr. Joseph Montgomery and Mrs. Montgomery invite you to a Children's Party to be held on the Rectory Croquet Lawns, etc . . . etc. . . ."

When return invitations came Pepper Tree Bay hostesses could hardly be expected to invite the whole tribe of us. So the token invitation was sent to the eldest—Vicky.

Vicky was dolled and prissed up, and there is no wonder in me that my mother's heart softened to water when she saw her eldest

55

daughter ready for a party. Vicky had several natural advantages over us all. She had thick curly hair, small delicate features and soft blue eyes. And she was shy and nervous, generally speaking; she was clinging. Also she was a very good little girl. It was a pleasure to invite Vicky to a decorous well-bred party. The same couldn't have been said for me or Denney or Gerry.

When the final crash came to our life and home there was a general feeling of relief that no harm could come to Vicky. The Bastons would see to that.

Such an attitude on our part was both stupid and ridiculous but it gave us a sense of security. We also felt vaguely that the world was full of other good people, and if necessary, they would look after the rest of us. Where such fanciful notions came from I have no idea, except that in our short lives we had so often seen our father and mother go to people's aid. I suppose we thought that help would come to us as simply and freely.

Thus there was no fear in our hearts when the time came for Mother to look around and wonder what she would do with five children under fifteen years of age, no home and no bread-winner. She assured us that all would be well, and we believed her.

We simply never dreamed the whole population of Pepper Tree Bay would forget our existence overnight.

All, that is, except the Bastons. They remained close friends and devoted to Vicky. We went on adoring them, but they came forward with no material advice. They simply hadn't an idea in their heads. My mother was utterly alone.

The Church sent her a polite letter saying it did not wish to hurry her—indeed please take what time was necessary—but the Rectory was needed for the new incumbent to the parish.

There was no insurance, pension or honorarium. My father's services to the Church had come to an end. Out!

The combined Mothers' Union, Girls' Friendly Society and Parish Women's Auxiliary gave my mother a farewell party and a presentation cheque of £100. It was wealth to us, for we were penniless.

Then everyone waited for us to go.

Mother cast around her frantically.

What should she do? What *could* she do?

Her first thought was to use her nursing experience. She hoped to remain in Pepper Tree Bay where she was known and where she thought her friends would support any hospital venture she might undertake.

It was I who accompanied her on the long, hot, dreadful walks around the big houses of Pepper Tree Bay looking for an empty one that was suitable and could be turned into a small private hospital.

I went gladly with my mother. It gave me a sense of importance. It also gave my mother some companionship, though I was never aware of that and never aware of her terrible fear of her own loneliness. She thought Vicky was not strong enough to go with her, so she suffered me rather than be alone. It was indeed a suffering, for my appearance—I had black straight hair and a mouth that was sometimes sulky—and my social graces were not Vicky's and I often irritated her to the point of active dislike.

Moreover, at the moment, I had a vested interest in our finding a house for a private hospital, and my mother knew it and disapproved. I was only thirteen, but I had a boy friend.

"Mama," I said. "That big house on the hill near the Convent would do. It's a lovely

big house. It's near Tom Jones's place too,"
or

"Mama, Tom Jones told me there's a house
over Swanbourne way on the other side of the
College."

"That's near Tom Jones's place too, I suppose?"

"Well, what if it is?" I asked sulkily.

"It doesn't matter a scrap that I can't get a
lease of either of those houses! Or that the
plumbing would cost £1,000 and we have
only £69 left?"

All the life of my young heart was taken up
with the business of loving Tom Jones. And
the lovely, impossible, astounding thing was
that Tom Jones loved me too.

The important thing about all this was that
Tom Jones was something of a figure in the
boy-girl world of Pepper Tree Bay. He went
to Scotch College and was the Champion Athlete. He became the Junior Champion
Athlete at the Inter School Sports and won
several open events too. Tom was now in demand by all the big and social houses around
Perth. He was ogled by a hundred girls. He
was spoken of in hushed whispers, for not only
did he achieve success in the sporting field
but he was an outstanding scholar. At the age

of fifteen he had passed his Matriculation Examination to the University. He was too young to be accepted at the University but the legend of his scholastic abilities grew side by side with his accumulating successes on the running field. Yet about all these things Tom was modest. I never heard him mention sport or scholarship.

All that mattered to Tom was that we understood the same things. We both knew there was a secret life beneath the seaweeds of Butler's Swamp. We were each of us aware of the deep throbbing life in the hills and valleys, by the creeks and under the ancient twisted gums of the most ancient and desolately lonely land of the earth. In conscious form we summed up this in an avowed liking for swimming, bush-walking, picnicking in the hills where we competed in gilgie hunts. We knew nothing about those strange inner stirrings, we only knew we sought one another's company instinctively.

When we were at a school dance one night, he kissed me.

It was a silly, frightened, pointless kiss. It was given and taken with terrific embarrassment on both sides. It was like the exchange of a token. We never referred to it again and never repeated it, but we were glad that it had happened.

So, of course, I wanted to stay in Pepper Tree Bay. We loitered on for a few weeks, eating away the gift of £100.

One night we went to a musical evening given by some friends in Cottesloe. When it was time to go home, Vicky and Mary hurried off to catch the train, but Tom and I loitered along the road and missed it. We made good use of the next half an hour until we thought the next train was due by sitting in the sand-dunes by the beach and holding hands. When we went for the train we found the one Vicky and Mary had caught was the last and there was nothing for it but to walk the four miles home.

We didn't mind. The night was lovely and we were young, and pitiably innocent. We knew nothing about sex whatever, so we could not understand why my mother was furious and gave me a beating in front of Tom. I hated her badly about that for a long time.

"What were you doing while you were waiting for what you thought was the next train?"

"We were sitting in the sand-hills talking."

61

"Were you doing anything else?"

I mumbled sulkily.

"What were you doing?" she persisted.

"Nothing. Just talking."

"Is that all?"

"Just holding hands . . ." I said suddenly. Why shouldn't she know that Tom Jones loved me. *She* didn't love me, but he did!

"Did Tom kiss you?"

"No."

"You are telling me the truth, Theodora?"

"He did once. But not to-night."

My mother paused, her hands in her lap, her face a curious study. She was silent for a long time.

"What's wrong with kissing anyway?" I demanded aggressively.

"Nothing. But you shouldn't do it," she said. "It leads to other things."

"Leads to what things?"

"You're too young to understand, Theodora, but you're not to do it. You must promise me. It leads to things that are very serious. You'll understand when you're grown up."

What things could kissing Tom Jones lead to, I wondered as I crawled to bed? I hadn't even a clue and presently I fell asleep and forgot all about it.

The next day my mother said she would take me to Perth. She had an appointment with a very important gentleman. She was trying this interview as a desperate move to settle what she could do about us all.

My mother took extra care with her dressing. When I was ready she looked at me disconsolately. She puckered up her mouth and bit the bottom lip as she always did when thinking deeply.

"You look a proper fright," she said at last. "That dress is too tight round the waist and you're all stomach. Go and put on Vicky's blue silk dress."

I didn't mind putting on Vicky's blue silk dress at all. It was the prettiest dress I had ever seen. Susan Baston had given her the material for a Christmas present.

"That's better," Mother said. "You look very nice now and it does at least cover up that terrible stomach. How on earth you come by such a big stomach I don't know."

I put my hands on my stomach and a dreadful—an annihilating thought came into my head.

Ladies who were going to have babies had big stomachs!

Is that what my mother meant when she

said kissing led to things? I had kissed Tom Jones!

The train journey to Perth, usually a treat, was purgatory. I wallowed in terror and misery.

The day was flat with heat and the sky a white glare in the eyes. The grey scrub along the railway embankment lamented in intermittent clumps between the stretches of barren grey sand. It was early spring but already the wild oats were yellow crackling stalks. "Fit only for blackfellows," my father would have said. At intervals the suburban towns were a scatter of sprawling ramshackle houses with the paint peeling from their iron roofs.

My mother was too preoccupied with her coming interview and too worried by her terrible responsibility to notice anything was amiss with me.

With leaden feet I followed her through the streets of Perth to the gentleman's place of business. I sweated agony of terror through the long interview, hardly hearing a word of it. It was all about a house for boarders and five hundred pounds. When we came out my mother took me to a tea-shop and we had tea and hot toasted buns. She was crying but I didn't even care about her tears. I dared not cry. Whatever were her troubles mine were infinitely worse. Her disgrace was at least honourable. I clawed at the blue dress covering my stomach with buttery hands.

Then into this gale of misery that was sweeping the heart and mind of both my mother and myself came Susan and Margaret Baston, two splendid Spanish galleons, full sail.

Mother surreptitiously wiped her eyes and prepared a bland expression. She moved her tea-things as if to make room at our table for her friends. But there was nothing but indignation on the Bastons' faces.

They glared at us, and their voices, always sharp with the arrogance of those who consciously carry full purses, could be heard as they moved towards another table.

"Vicky's dress!"

For the first time I realised how dictatorial and possessive was the Baston attitude towards us.

Mother hearing the remark looked with a mixed air of irritation and embarrassment at the dress.

"Margaret and Susan have never wanted for dresses," she said to me. "Else they too might have worn one another's."

She was filled with pity for me that I should bear this ignominy. She did not dream how little I was affected by this scene. I had worse troubles on my mind.

She began to gather up her gloves and bag, for she intended to pass the Bastons with the same frigid acknowledgment they had afforded us.

"You children will never accept another expensive present again," she said. "It has always been a humiliation to me, though I've pretended for your sakes it was all right to accept so much. Now we will fight our own battles. What we can't buy we'll go without."

These were fine sentiments of Mama's and she lived up to them for her own sake, yet she forgave Susan and Margaret almost before she left the shop. Even in the moment of her greatest anger she did not forget the genuine generosity that inspired so many of their actions towards children. She herself was incapable of harbouring rancour.

It seemed as if it was on this very day that Mama ceased to think of the world as peopled with those who were kindly disposed towards herself. From now on she saw life differently.

"The only things we will ever have in this life are the things we ourselves will pay for," she said. Then she had one of her awful sentimental moments which often spoiled her more noble ideas.

"We have a long way to go before we again have a place in society." She sighed and picked up the chit and left the table. "The road winds uphill all the way." She could not remember where she had heard that line but as she said it she quite visibly straightened her shoulders and carried her head a little higher. The stripe the Bastons had given her had flayed her to greater courage.

On the train back to Pepper Tree Bay she told me that the gentleman we had seen had been very pleasant to her. He was a prominent Churchman and he and several others were going to finance her in buying a boarding-house in West Perth. They would give her five years to pay the money back and they didn't want any interest. The tears Mother had shed in the tea-shop had been tears of relief mingled with gratitude for the kindness of these men.

So bitter were my own fears, however, so selfish the ignorance of childhood, that I experienced no sense of relief.

For days, indeed I think a week or two, I went

67

about carrying my private dread. My mind planned endlessly some means of escape and secrecy. Perhaps I could go to the country where no one knew me. Perhaps I could get a job as a servant on a sheep station so many miles into the North-west that no one would be able to dismiss me out of hand. Though I thought it quite possible that someone would engage a thirteen-year-old girl as a servant, I didn't think it was likely that so young a person would be turned out into the desert to die of thirst and sunstroke. Though sometimes I went through that fantasy of terror too.

There came, of course, a morning when I could not eat a vestige of breakfast.

"That child seems off colour every morning," Mother said.

I stared at her, speechless. Somewhere I had heard or seen written that women going to have babies were sick in the mornings. If there had been the slightest vestige of doubt in my mind it had fled now.

I picked up my school case and went out of the door. Somehow, in a kind of stupor, I found my way to school. It was term examination time and I had to take my place in the examination hall. I stared with blurred eyes at the paper. I could not read it. I hadn't done any work, or opened a book for days and nights and I knew nothing. My empty stomach began to rumble and remind me of itself. Suddenly the whole thing was too much for me. The blood rushed to my head and then receded. The walls of the hall began to take on a slant; the desk in front of me slipped sideways crazily and I had a terrible thwack on the side of the head.

In a moment the teacher was beside me and I was being lifted up and carried outside. Still too terrified to say anything I lay on the lounge in the Community Room and could not get my parched lips to form an answer when the sisters and the school nurse spoke to me.

At last Sister Rowena telephoned my mother and I was sent home in the school car. My mother put me to bed and called in Dr. Riley.

I lay in anguish waiting for him.

"She hasn't been eating for two or three weeks," Mother said when he finally came. "This morning she went off without any breakfast at all. No wonder she fainted."

Dr. Riley took the thermometer out of my mouth and looked puzzled.

"Pull up your shirt, missy," he said kindly.

69

"I'll have a look at that tummy of yours and see if that's what's giving you a white tongue."

If only I could die, pass away! God would forgive me because He would know that I hadn't known that a kiss would "lead to things." But my mother and the neighbours and all the people in Pepper Tree Bay would never forgive me. Dr. Riley tapped and prodded and pushed. At last he straightened up. I opened my eyes.

"Don't look so frightened," he said with a smile. "There's nothing much wrong with you, you know." He turned to Mother. "There's a fair bit of wind in the stomach, that's all. Nervous dyspepsia, I should say."

"Only wind in my stomach?" I asked. My voice cracked badly.

Doctor Tim pinched his nose between his thumb and forefinger.

"Wind, that's all," he said. "We can soon fix that with some white powders." He turned to my mother.

"Has she been over-working? Over-worried? Had a fright?"

My mother shook her head sadly, thinking I had really been sharing her worries.

"I think it's all been too much for the poor

child," she said. As they went out the door I heard her recounting the humiliation she thought I felt when the Bastons had been so angry with me in the little tea-shop.

I lay on my back staring out of the window.

Could it really be true? No baby? No disgrace?

Were those the same gum trees I had been looking at for days and days?

How blue the skies were! How beautifully the sun shone!

The sounds of the world were enthralling and wonderful beyond belief.

Oh shining, happy world! My world! Theodora's world!

But I would never kiss a boy again as long as I lived.

6

THE WAY TO SCHOOL

THERE remained only one more thing to brim my cup of happiness to overflowing. How resilient one was as a child and how little one understood or really shared our mother's troubles! Yet I wanted success for her more than I did for myself. For myself I only wanted to be left alone to contemplate the strange and moving things of the bush; to feel that the cloud piles in a stormy sky were mine and that some day, when I was grown-up, I would make of all this magic something of my own.

The means of finding a home were settled, the bonds with Pepper Tree Bay were psychologically severed—the problem now was how the means were to be found to keep me at school for another year or two until I passed the examinations which would give me some scholastic standing in the world at large. Mother was still intent on making me a schoolteacher.

One day, a week after my notable faint, the angels of God whispered in the ears of the two principal sisters of the school.

"Now Theodora, my child," said Sister Verna in her quiet, old, but infinitely gentle voice. "You know that Mary Denning is leaving school to finish her education abroad?"

"Yes, Sister Verna."

"She is a very good girl," she said vaguely. "A very good girl indeed. We are proud of her."

"Yes, Sister Verna."

Her attention came back to me.

"She's held the scholarship for clergymen's daughters for four years," she said.

"And a great credit she has been to it," put in Sister Rowena in a very determined voice.

"We think, Sister Rowena and I think, you could win that scholarship now that it is vacant."

"Oh, Sister Verna," I cried. "Could I? Could I?"

"Don't fidget, child," she said. "And your voice is getting squeaky. Keep it down. Remember what King Lear said of Cordelia, 'Her voice was ever soft, gentle and low, an excellent thing in woman'." She poised her pencil over her pad and looked at me closely.

"I don't think you could be anything like as good a girl as Mary Denning, but you could at least *try*."

Sister Verna smiled gently.

"You must pass the examination, dear," she said. "After all, it is the headmistress who is the judge. There are thirty-nine clergymen's daughters here and they will all be set an examination in their own form and the headmistress will judge which is the best performance. But Sister Rowena and I thought that if we warned you about it you might do a little extra work and try and help your poor mother as well as yourself."

"Oh yes, Sister, I will," I said. "I promise you."

"No hockey for the rest of the term," said Sister Rowena.

"Oh no, Sister. I'll work hard I promise you."

I hurried home after school to tell Mother. She looked at me with eyes that dared not hope.

"Oh, Theodora, could you do it? Could you win it?"

"I think I can . . . at least I'll work hard."

I didn't feel anything like as airy as my words. I had begun to think of the other girls

74

in the school who would be working just as desperately hard and who numbered some quite clever ones amongst them.

Mother plunged her floury hands into the pudding-basin. She was thinking of my faint.

"It doesn't matter, Theodora, if you don't win it. We wouldn't be any worse off. We would be just the same as if Mary Denning wasn't going to England.

"But if you could win it . . . if you could. . . ."

I started straight away on a routine of work. I had all the good-will and resolution in the world. I hadn't any idea what subjects they would choose to examine as this was kept a secret and so I had to "swot" everything we took in classwork.

Resolutions were one thing, but a flagging spirit and restive body was another. I would sit all hours of the night with sleep-weary eyes over books I could hardly read and with an interest I couldn't force. I rose early in the morning, but my gaze would wander from the French grammar to the dew spangling the grass and to the first magpies in the gum-trees. I realised within a week or two I wasn't doing anything like the amount of work I should do and that I lacked the necessary powers of concentration.

Every night when I went to bed I prayed. "Please God, let me win. It doesn't matter a fig about me. I know I'm not a good girl and You probably don't even like me. But please don't think about *me*, think about *Mother*."

At the same time Mary was working for a Government Scholarship that would take her to the big high school. When I saw her neatly set-out notebooks and compared them with mine, rough and ink-stained; when I saw her head bent relentlessly over her studies, never once letting her eyes stray and with nothing of the restiveness in her body that was an agony in mine, I felt sure that she would win her scholarship. She, at least, would be a credit to Mother. I knew that and would flay myself into a renewed burst of work. But every time I found myself happy and enthralled it was in the subjects at which I was already quite proficient. French, Algebra and Arithmetic were as much stumbling-blocks as ever. Ancient History, a subject I loved but which was generally considered unimportant in the curriculum, I hardly touched. It had only been added as a "frill" to our education and not taken seriously because it was not set as a subject in the Public Examinations.

The day came for the examination. The three of us in my class who were taking it were set a mathematics paper in three sections, one section each in Arithmetic, Algebra and Geometry. We had to do eight questions altogether with at least one in each section. I did the required one in Algebra and Arithmetic and did the other six questions in Geometry. When we compared notes I had the Arithmetic wrong, the Algebra right and I wasn't sure about the Geometry. The answers of the others certainly didn't agree with mine.

In the afternoon we had the second paper. It consisted of one question. . . .

"Write a Literary Essay on the Punic Wars."

Ancient History and I hadn't touched it! I was aghast. Then with my usual volatile change of mood I turned from sick despair to irrational anger. I flew at the essay like a thing possessed with rage, one which drove me into a furious flow of unchecked prose. I gave the Punic Wars and Hannibal something to think about. At all events I produced the extraordinary vocabulary I had learned from my father's rhetoric, and I thought angrily if irreverently . . . "I'll make the damn' thing Literary if I can't make it Historical."

A day or two later when my class was doing prep, I noticed the science teacher smiling and chuckling to herself as she turned over some closely-written pages. Each time a girl went to the desk she covered up the pages. Something about the heavy inky outline of the writing, as seen through the thin pages, seemed familiar to me. What of mine had the science mistress got hold of? Could ... could it be that the headmistress had let her read my essay on the Punic Wars? And why was she chuckling? I had never written anything clever or funny in my life. She must be laughing AT it. I was full of rage and shame.

The next day I saw the essay folded once longways in a book the English mistress carried. In the afternoon the maths teacher made a joke about a "lion seizing its prey" and then she looked at me and smiled. The joke rang a bell. I had said something about Hannibal descending on his enemies "Like a lion to seize its prey."

Two weeks went by and there was no announcement. I still prayed fervently about the examination.

Then came Mary's news. She had won her

scholarship; one much harder and more competitive than mine. She would go the next year to the high school and all tuition, fares and books paid. Well, thank God, someone in the family would be something of a charge off Mother's hands. I didn't feel so bad about the prospect of failing now. After all Mother had achieved something in Mary's win.

A day or two later I came home from school to be met with Mother's radiant face. She waved a letter.

"They've written to me," she said. "You've won it."

I was awe-inspired. I hadn't believed that God really cared about us, but evidently He did.

For a few days I couldn't really believe that I had won, and even in the privacy of my mind I did not give myself any airs. I remembered God's part in the business and I thanked Him in my prayers.

"I know you did it for Mother and it wasn't really for me. I know Sister Verna and Sister Rowena put it into your mind, and I do thank you for Mother's sake."

The only comment I ever heard from

school about the examination was one from the headmistress long afterwards.

"When I am old and retired," she said, "there's one thing I'll take out of this school with me, and I shall frame it and keep it on my drawing-room wall. That is Theodora Montgomery's essay on the Punic Wars."

7

FAREWELL TO ALL THAT

WE left Pepper Tree Bay without the thunder of guns or the waving of flags.

We, Mother and her five children, walked to the railway station about three-quarters of a mile away. Mother would have liked to have hired Williams' cab as a last show of dignity, but even her pride could not hold its place against the immediate and stark need of the family. We had literally been eating, in much reduced meals, the hundred pounds' presentation money.

We walked slowly in the fatigue of nostalgia. Mother, I think, was weary beyond words. She neither knew nor cared that no one had come to see us off; no one had realised that this day marked her departure from a parish to which she had given years of unremitting service. The light of the battle which she was yet to wage against life was not yet in her eyes.

I had looked back at the Rectory gates and at the old pepper trees we used to climb and from which I had declaimed my poetry and into whose leafy pungent scented shadows I had dreamed the foolish fantasies of childhood. I looked at the old derelict stables where Gerry had hidden for a day and a night amidst the spiders and scorpions of decayed wood to escape from Father's wrath after a running-away expedition. Denney and Gerry were terrors for running away. No lock or rope-end could stop them. My father, exasperated on one occasion, said he would put a stop to it. He took Denney and gave her a terrible thrashing, so dreadful that we were all frightened for her life. He then ordered Denney into bed.

"That will put an end to it," he declared. "There'll be no more running away now."

We listened in horrified silence to Denney's fearful sobs. My father rolled down his sleeves, put on his coat and went out. Presently the sounds from Denney's big iron cot subsided and Mother took a peep at her.

"Ssh! she's asleep," she whispered to us. "It was a terrible thrashing to give a little girl, but it will indeed stop her running away."

About an hour later the station-master from the railway rang Mother on the telephone.

"Have you, by any chance, a small girl missing? She's about four years old and is in pink pyjamas."

Mother gasped.

"Vicky, quick! Look in Denney's cot."

The station-master drawled on. . . .

"She answers by way of a name like Dennis. I've asked her what her father's name is and she says, 'The boys call him sir, but Mother only calls him Joe'."

Vicky had come running back.

"She's gone, Mama," she said.

"Is Williams' cab outside the station?" Mother asked the master. "Would you please put Denney on it and tell Mr. Williams to bring her home?"

My father walking down the Highway was astounded to behold Williams' cab making a triumphal progress in the direction of the Rectory, with Denney in pink pyjamas on the box beside the driver.

My father lifted his great hand and called a halt to this wickedness. What he intended to say no one knows, but old Williams told my mother the story later.

"The Reverend Joe looked fit to burst,

ma'am." he said. "Then all of a sudden he lets out the air in him and stands looking at that young nipper all quiet like. Then he puts his hand in his pocket and fetches out a half-crown.

"'How many stripes on your bottom, Denney?'"

There and then Denney had to turn herself over and show Mr. Williams what the strap had done to her seat and her legs.

"'There's half a crown for the stripes, Denney,'" said my father. Then he shook the stick under her nose.

"'I admire your spirit, my girl,' he said. 'And let no one say otherwise. But the prisons of Ireland and the evil lands of the world are full of the likes of you. You'll come to no good end . . . but I'll wash my hands of you now. What the strap won't cure reason will never mend.'"

Our leaving the Rectory was my own personal sorrow, Mother's tragic grief. That it meant anything to the others didn't occur to me.

Denney, of course, had to turn the affair into an adventure of her own.

Less than a third of the way along the Highway she remembered treasured pos-

84

sessions she had left under the pepper trees.

"Mama! My black Beth . . . I've left her under the pepper trees. And my bathers* too."

We all put down our cases and Mother looked at Denney with a mixture of exasperation and concern. Denney never went anywhere without her black rag doll and her bathers.

"Oh, for goodness' sake, Denney," said Mother weakly. "Go back and get them."

Out of the corner of her eye Denney looked at me. I knew at once that she had planned this arrangement. I knew instantly what would be Mother's next words

"Theodora, you're the strongest, pick up Denney's case. You'll have to carry them both. Denney, you run back hard while we go on. We don't want to miss the train."

Oh, the cunning of that little wretch! Even in this dire moment in our lives Denney thought of one more opportunity to score over me, knowing that Mother would pass the obligations over Vicky's delicate head and rest them on my shoulders. I would rather have committed murder than carry Denney's

*Swim-suit.

85

case, but Mother was obdurate. Her dreadful weariness and grief stood between me and the right to resist Denney.

I made one futile attempt which only rendered Denney's victory the greater.

"Mama, she's done it on purpose. She knew you would make me carry her case."

"Oh, you dreadful children," she cried bitterly. "Is this the moment for your wicked quarrelling? Pick up that case, Theodora. You know Vicky can't carry it, her heart is not as strong as yours and Mary's already doing all she can."

Mother's tears beat me. I picked up the case, but there was death in my heart for Denney. She saw it and her big violet eyes gleamed with joy as she savoured her victory.

Denney sped away on blithe feet.

Mother couldn't leave the subject alone then.

"You ought to be ashamed of yourself, Theodora. A great lump of a girl like you— always fighting with one so much younger. You're older than Denney, you ought to know better."

I did know better. But Denney knew better still. She knew how to chew her food loudly enough to madden me but not loudly enough to draw Mother's notice. When I was doing my homework, she would sit down beside me and breathe loudly against my neck. If I hit her, which was often, she screamed and Mother declared I was a bully.

"Mother," I cried once in dire torment. "Please, *please* stop Denney. She's *breathing*."

Mother put down her needlework and gazed at me with derisive laughter in her eyes.

"She's *breathing*! My goodness, how terrible to be *breathing*. How will she go on living if she doesn't breathe?"

"She's doing it on purpose."

"Don't you breathe on purpose?"

"She's doing it *aloud*."

"Oh, for goodness' sake, Theodora, have some sense. Why do you take any notice of Denney? She only does it to annoy you. You're so much older you ought to know better."

I screamed at them both and flung out of the room.

I heard Mother's voice through the wall.

"We really must do something about Theodora. She's too emotional."

I remembered the hundred times Mother had decided to cure me of being emotional by laughing at me and holding my moods up to scorn.

"So Ireland's aggrieved again . . ." she would say.

There was now, on this day, an extraordinary and painful conflict in my heart.

I was desperately sorry for her. I knew and understood her own humiliation and I grieved for her. At the same time I hated her because she could not understand mine and because she scorned me and held me up as a creature for ridicule.

These conflicting emotions were to colour all the rest of my life. I was bound to Mother, a reluctant and helpless prisoner. I was always over-awed by her phenomenal generosity, by her implacable resistance to the buffets of fate, by her relentless and sometimes stupid loyalty to her children, by her capacity for unremitting and often unrewarded work, by her sheer rock-like resistance to the forces of disintegration in a family such as ours. "We'll always stick together," was to become her perpetual slogan. That we did and have is an achievement the angels might have envied.

Up the long hill we trailed. Mother and Vicky first. Mother sometimes helping "poor Vicky." Myself next, soon forgetting Denney's case and its burden on my mood because I was enraptured by the new window display in Padden's Book Shop.

After me came Mary, preoccupied, silent, anxiously dutiful, chewing thoughtfully at her beautiful china-doll mouth.

When we came to the station and I saw much of our baggage waiting for the luggage-van, the hockey sticks reminded me of Mary.

In one of the thundering rows that Father and Mother sometimes had Mother had begun to cry. Ashamed before the children she went to the bathroom and Father made as if to follow her. When he got to the end of the passage Mary was standing in the doorway with the hockey stick in her hand. She was eight. Her hair hung sideways over her eyes and her head bent slightly forward. Her feet were planted apart and she grasped the hockey stick in her right hand. There was no fear or panic or temper in her.

"You leave her alone," she said to my father.

He was thunder-struck.

For an awful moment nobody quite knew what would happen, though I quite expected nothing short of death for Mary.

"Get out of my way," shouted my father.

"By all the sins of the dead and the damned! To be confronted by a brat like you!"

Mary did not budge.

"You leave her alone," she said, tightening her grip on the hockey stick.

She had courage . . . and blinding loyalty to my mother. To defy this dealer of almost death-like blows was to place herself in the path of a mad bull in a paddock.

Fortunately my mother realised what Mary was doing. She saw the look of terrible rage on my father's face as he towered over Mary, still standing stalwart and unafraid.

Mother moved quickly along the veranda and pulled Mary behind her back.

"Don't touch her," she warned. Mary and hockey stick began to struggle against Mother's restraining hand behind her back.

"If you touch her, I leave the house to-day," Mother said. Something in her voice brought my father back to sanity. Whatever wild useless and pointless threats Mother had used in the past were not to be compared with the ring of determination that was now in her voice. We all knew, with absolute certitude, that if Father laid a finger on Mary we would have gone forth from the Rectory that very day.

My father threw back his head and passed his hand over his hair.

"Take the little tartar out of my sight," he shouted with an attempt at arrogance that was merely theatrical. He turned and stamped up the passage.

"In the ould country," he orated, "they would have jailed a woman for less. Turning the hearts and minds of little children against their own father. . . ." One could hear the tears of self-pity in the thickness of his Irish tongue.

Mary sat on the station now, isolated from the others in my thoughts by that one act of loyalty and bravery.

We sat in a row, miserable, tired, dejected.

All except Gerry. She slid off the wooden seat and surveyed the other passengers waiting for the train. She was selecting her victim.

"Where are you going?" she said to an elderly man leaning on his stick and puffing an ancient pipe.

"What's that to you, little girl?"

"Are you going to Perth?"

The man surveyed her in silence. Gerry tried another tack.

"What's your name?"

"What's yours?"

"Geraldine Rory Montgomery and those are my sisters . . . Victoria Yvonne Montgomery, Theodora Eileen Montgomery, Mary Cathleen Montgomery and Denney Shannon Montgomery. My mother's name is Mrs. Montgomery."

The man looked bewildered.

"I think you had better go back to your mother, little girl."

Gerry sighed. She moved farther up the platform to a woman with a large dress basket.

"What's that?" asked Gerry.

"A basket."

"What's in it?"

"All sorts of things. What's your name, little girl?"

"Geraldine Rory Montgomery. What's yours?"

"You're a funny little girl, aren't you?"

"No, I'm not," said Gerry, "I'm only being politely interested in your basket. Just to make conversation, you know. That's my mother over there. She's Mrs. Montgomery and those are my sisters . . . Victoria Yvonne Montgomery, Theodora Eileen Montgomery,

Mary Cathleen Montgomery and Denney Shannon Montgomery. Denney runs away and my father thrashed her once and my mother tied her up with a rope. We thought she'd miss the train to-day because she had to go back for Black Beth and the bathers. But she got here on time."

The woman was looking at Mother out of puzzled wondering eyes.

"Come here, Gerry," Mother commanded. Gerry ignored her.

"We're going to live in West Perth," Gerry went on. "Where are you going?"

"I'm going home."

"Do you live in a boarding-house? We do now."

Mother crossed the platform. She gave the woman a wan smile as she took Gerry's hand.

"She's full of questions," Mother said apologetically.

"All children are like that," said the woman, sympathetic but curious.

"Good-bye," said Gerry with a friendly smile. "I'll be looking for you on the train."

Mother dragged Gerry away. She was itching to slap Gerry who was preening herself in the sunshine of everyone's attention.

A man came and sat on the seat next to us.

"Have you got a dog?" Gerry began.

Fortunately the train whistled and we all began to sort out our cases.

"We're going first-class," Gerry announced regretfully as she was dragged in the opposite direction from the man about whose mythical dog she had suddenly become interested.

It was true. We were going first-class. Mother couldn't afford a cab to the station but she would not have sailed out of Pepper Tree Bay second-class if the difference in fares had cost us our last penny. And it very nearly did.

"We're all together now," she said as we settled in an empty carriage. "This is a new life, children. Whatever happens we must stick together. United we are strong."

"Up the Montgomerys!" said Denney wickedly.

I felt embarrassed. I longed fiercely for no one to notice, not even ourselves, that with the jerk of the train we were leaving Pepper Tree Bay for ever.

8

THE BOARDING-HOUSE

THE boarding-house was a large two-story affair. It had been built in the palmier days of the late colonial era and its rooms were big and high; the brickwork solid and enduring. This main edifice had been encrusted with wooden verandas and balconies.

Most of this woodwork had fallen a waste to white ants and none of it had been repainted in fifteen years. Inside the paper peeled from the walls and the plaster dropped from the ceilings.

A main passage passed straight through the house from the front door; on either side of this passage were three large rooms. The passage ended in a small living-room which was one of the wooden adjuncts to the house. On the left of this was a large dark kitchen and on the left again, after passing through the kitchen, an enormous scullery.

The upper story of the original brick building was almost the replica of the lower story. On either side of the passage there were two big rooms and where there was a third room below, on the story above there were small servants' rooms and bathrooms. . . . The passage ended in the front upper story in a long french window that opened on to the balcony. The balcony itself was blinded off in three parts, one each to the rooms opening on to the balcony and a small between-space entered upon from the passage door. This screened-off part of the passage and the small portion of middle balcony was the extent of privacy achieved by Vicky, Mary and myself. Mary and I slept on the balcony and Vicky in the narrow bed behind the curtain in the passage.

This arrangement must have been hideous to Mary and Vicky. I can't remember that I cared much one way or the other about where I had to sleep or live. The other two were different, however. Vicky had treasures of gloves, belts, stockings, silver-backed brushes and some nice clothes, relics of the Bastons' generosity. Mary was fanatically tidy and the love of her possessions obsessed her. I had no possessions.

All my treasures were in my head. The only thing I needed to have some home for was a thing about which I was more ashamed than proud. A thing that was a secret, a furtive skulking secret, which I kept locked up in an old trunk in the bottom of the cellar. It was a notebook. I sometimes wrote poetry in it. Shockingly bad poetry too.

On the ground floor Mother and Denney and Gerry lived in one of the little wooden back-rooms built on to the rear of the house.

Mother had taken over "Forty-five" as a going concern so that when we moved in it was to a house full of curious people. Most of them were business men and women and they eyed us not unkindly but with considerable apprehension. Five young noisy girls thus descending upon them was enough to give cause for wonder. The woman who sold the goodwill of the house to Mother had been a professional boarding-house keeper all her life. Suddenly we, the Montgomerys, arrived to take over. Undoubtedly the boarders must all have known our story, but even so they were a little startled by our airs, by Mother's pretentious insistence on living the life of a "lady," at least as far as outward appearances were concerned. That house was kept scrubbed and polished but no one ever saw Mother in the actual role of char—she waited until everyone was out.

These people were not anything like as concerned about our pretensions, however, as they were as to how our impact was going to affect their food and comfort. Their uneasiness about this aspect of affairs was nothing in comparison with Mother's.

She had cooked big meals before. They had been elegant dinner-parties or family dinners. How was she to cook meals which would satisfy these people?

We had taken over on a Saturday and the evening dinner was to be the testing-point. One felt the atmosphere of concern and expectancy on the boarders' part and of nervousness on my mother's.

She need not have worried. She was a good cook and she had no inclination or experience in the cheese-paring economies of boarding-house keepers. She prepared a dinner fit for my father's Rectory dinner-table when he was entertaining the school staff.

When the fateful meal was over, one of the boarders, a thin nervous saleswoman in one of the big stores of Perth came into the kitchen. She was rubbing her hands with pleasure.

"Oh, Mrs. Montgomery," she said. "That was a lovely dinner. What a good cook you are!"

Mother gazed at her. About the narrow head of this kindly little saleswoman there suddenly glowed a halo and her flat thin cheeks took on the radiance of beauty and charm. Tears of gratitude came into my mother's eyes. Never was a compliment more humbly or gratefully taken.

Thereafter Miss Hatchers was the star boarder. The best cut was always kept for her. On Sundays her breakfast was taken to her in bed and when she had a cold my mother nursed her as if she were one of her own.

In the front room were two bachelors. One day, Vicky, who made the beds and did the bachelors' room, found a hair pin in one of the beds. Not a word was said about it, but after that Mother did the bachelors' room, and we gathered that they were bad men, not to be met with on dark nights, and not to be seen chatting with on week-ends.

All these people were very ordinary people and, the bachelors included, kind, natural, easy people to live with. Yet to us they were indefinably the "boarders," people whose existence were symbols of our humiliation, of our downward slide from the fashionable world.

To them we must have seemed rather ludicrous upstarts. However there was nothing in their hearts but admiration for and gratitude to my mother for her great feats of work and endurance and the loving consistent care she took of those amongst them who were sick or who she thought worked too hard or were lonely and depressed.

This vast house, with its heterogeneous collection of souls, twenty in all, was worked without domestic help. Mother cooked, cleaned, washed, scrubbed, till the shabby old place shone as much as human hands could make it do so. We three eldest took a hand in washing and turning curtains, recovering cushions and upholstering butter-boxes to brighten the rooms. Mary at twelve could cook a dinner or take hammer and chintz to a butter-box as ably as anyone.

Vicky, at this period, was Mother's right hand. She was taken away from school and sent to business college to learn shorthand and typewriting. She didn't have to be at the college till ten in the morning and before she left she made all the beds in the house—except in the bachelors' room—and together with Mother washed up the huge piles of breakfast dishes. My job consisted mostly of cutting all the lunches for the family. After school Mary cut the firewood and laid the fires and swept the yard. The three of us did the enormous washing-up after dinner at night, but we quarrelled furiously and relentlessly about "turns."

I did least to help because it had been decided that I should take two years' work in one year in order to get my Leaving Certificate and qualify to become a teacher.

I wish I could think I used that extra time honourably. I did in fact spend long hours sitting in front of my books. Many I read with pleasure and avidity, but they were always the same subjects . . . the ones I loved. When it came to struggling with the difficult and distasteful I loafed.

To be cloistered in a shabby over-crowded room in a second-rate boarding-house while the red and gold of an Australian sunset set fingers of fire stealing through the prickling crackling undergrowth was more than could often be endured.

But when night and silence came I could come in from the backyard and out of the stillness of the black, velvet-domed, star-ridden Australian night and I would take a book and play truant from my own country. At night-time I didn't live in Australia, I lived in the Doone Valley; I knew intimately the Master of Ballantrae; with Nicholas Nickleby I endured the horrors of Dotheboys Hall; and I knew every resident of the Cathedral Close at Barchester. Above all I was lulled to sleep in the arms of Rupert Brooke.

The first year at "Forty-five" was a painful jumbled year. Pain because of so much we had lost, jumbled because of our difficulty in reassessing our values, the whole a struggle against background and against poverty.

Enough livelihood had been won in that year to keep us alive but our clothes were worn to raggedness, our needs became greater as we became older, and Mother's ambition for us never flagged. We were the "shabby genteel" and we tried to put on the faces of comfortably placed gentlewomen.

Vicky had achieved enough practice in typewriting at the end of six months to secure herself a post as an underpaid secretary at a college. I was to finish my education and become a school-teacher, Mary had already formed the ambition to become a lawyer and she clung tenaciously to her choice. Such ambition may have seemed madness to some, but not to the Montgomerys. The fact that the Law was a profession that required years of training, large sums of capital for Articles or entry into a "Firm"; that the men in the profession would close their ranks against the women; that maintenance was required to provide food, clothing, books and fares for the next ten years were matters airily waved away by the Montgomerys. Mary *would* become a lawyer, and . . . so help me God, she did. By scholarships, by coaching dullards in her spare time, by sitting in the cash desk of a jeweller's shop in vacations, by walking to the university instead of taking the tram, by going without her lunches and mostly by warding off the many, many young men who hungered after that red provocative mouth of hers, Mary became a lawyer.

Denney and Gerry were still children in this our first year at "Forty-five." The years were yet to show what ambitions Mother could harbour for them. For herself, she sought only to work hard enough and live long enough to see her children's feet set well upon the road of social recovery. The only unworthy thing about her planning and dreaming was the false value she set upon social standards. In truth it was only when we came to live at "Forty-five" that we entered the real and living world.

Mother's kindness and attention to others knew no bounds and yet it was never entirely divorced from her fixed attitudes of the old Rectory days. She was still the Lady of the Village distributing the largess of her bounteous nature upon the needy. Her children never dreamed that in her fierce maternity there was less of the cradling, murmuring mother, and more of the relentless tiger fighting for her offspring's rights in a society of which she still had Victorian ideas.

At the end of the first year she needed money for all our clothes, for Mary's extra books. Mother went the rounds of the private hospitals asking for odd nursing work. This was readily accorded but the kind of jobs she got were those that staff nurses sheered away from—night duty with the dying; the laying out of the dead.

Mother would return to "Forty-five" after twelve hours' night duty at a private hospital to start cleaning, polishing, scrubbing, cooking for the boarding-house.

God knows how she did it and kept her health and sanity.

Part Two

Part Two

1

FAMILY GROWING PAINS

FIVE years at "Forty-five" produced changes in our life.

Gradually Mother converted the house from a boarding establishment to one of flatlets. For ourselves we salvaged the use of the big downstairs room on the right of the passage as a dining-room. Though we had lost the "boarders," we had scarcely lost in numbers as the family sat down to a meal. Vicky, Mary and I had grown to the age when we were interested in the young men of the University and their friends. Moreover, and what was most gratifying, the young men were interested in us. To the students living in hostels the Montgomery household was a haven. It was somewhere to go and sit. Somewhere to have a meal and where there was plenty of noise, and the flash of personalities chipping sparks off personalities which were too much alike for there to be any real peace.

At the Montgomery house there were always girls to take out to the dances or tennis matches, or to the pictures.

The years, even so, were hard because we had to work hard. And mostly we worked in a milling vociferous crowd. Affairs of the world by day and deadly chores by night and on Saturdays. We made our own clothes. We patched and darned and turned old garments. Mary always achieved a model bandbox appearance by sheer hard work and artistry. Vicky and Denney did well enough too.

In the ancient clothes remodelled and remodelled again, we three eldest managed to go to all the dances and fashionable tennis tournaments, and sun-baking on the beach. And we didn't mind much that we went about with girls dressed by Perth's best dressmakers. We were secure in our knowledge of being a family of great worth and quite unique. We were only saved from being impossible by our capacity for endless work and our gargantuan sense of laughter and of the ridiculous. When it came to sniping at the Montgomerys we got in first.

Only Mother didn't see the funny side of pretending to keep up a social position reminiscent of the old Rectory days. The name Montgomery carried an aura of prestige for her. Any prestige that was about should have gathered around her own character of great worth, but she interpreted it always in terms of my father's illustrious past in the green isle over the seas. She remained resolutely faithful to the memory of the "cultured gentry." Even we couldn't laugh her out of her wedlock with that most cruel of all tyrants . . . the Keeper-up of Appearances.

On this Saturday we were, as on all Saturdays, choring.

Gerry bending over the sewing machine was talking too much and she caught the material in the shuttle.

"Hell and damnation!" she exploded.

Mother was in the throes of making the kind of sponge cake that takes a step-ladder to reach.

"Don't use such dreadful language," she said. "How is it a young girl like you has learned to swear like that!"

"I'm surprised a good woman like you knows the meaning of the words." Mother's egg whisk was halted in half-flight.

"She didn't *know*," I said. "She had knowledge thrust upon her by her family." I caught Mother's eyes and she could not help the little smile that crept from her lips to her eyes.

"We live and learn," she said. "I was bent on giving you girls an education, but it seems you have become the educators and me the dunce in the corner."

"Bust and blow," said Gerry with exaggerated docility as she failed to free the shuttle. "Dash and darn!" It was more provocative than her cursing and Mother was getting ready to be angry again.

"Talking of darns . . ." I said pointing with a knife at the hole in the heel of Mother's stocking. "When did you last see your needle?"

"Great Heavenly Ghost!" she looked at it in horror.

"*Mother,*" we all screamed. "*You blasphemed!*"

"I'll put bull-frogs on your grave," said Gerry tersely. Of all the sounds in the night Mother loathed bull-frogs above others.

"Never mind, Mummy darling," said Vicky leaving the sink and putting her arms around Mother. No wonder Mother loved her the best! Vicky was always there with her soft words at the right moment.

"How many to lunch?"

"Evan will be here for sure," said Mary, "and you're going to the Rottnest in the launch with Bill Jennings, so I guess he'll be here too."

"Only two extra for Sunday lunch?" said Mother. "That's a change. Theodora, you go and get ready. I'll finish the salad."

Evan Burns was Mary's friend and admirer. He was an immigrant Scot of the business man variety, alone in the world, and he had made almost a second home of "Forty-five." We pretended to be bored by him so that Mary wouldn't get ideas because she had an admirer ten years older than herself and quite a man of the world. Bill Jennings, a cadet journalist on the *West Australian*, was a friend of mine. We disliked one another actively but went nearly everywhere together. We pretended it was because we liked to practise our witticisms on each other's thick skins. He was nearly part of the family too.

On this day we joined a launch party to the island twelve miles off the coast. The crossing both ways was choppy and I wasn't a good sailor. I had a splitting headache all the time. To make things worse, Bill told me he was making the trip for the "paper" and that we'd got free tickets.

I came home feeling much the worse for wear.

"What do you think?" I demanded bitterly. "We weren't honoured guests on the *Merlin* at all. Bill had *free* tickets."

"Well, what of it?" said Mother. "The thing is you got there."

"But I didn't want to go. It was a rotten trip, and Bill bores me."

"You're never satisfied, Theodora," Mother said. "Lots of girls would be happy to go out with a nice boy like Bill."

"Then why don't they? I'm not stopping them."

"Is he staying for dinner?"

"Try and move him. He's in the one and only decent armchair and not even waiting to be asked."

"He doesn't have to," said Mother sternly. "I sometimes think you girls are very ungracious."

I shrugged my shoulders. I was completely graceless to-day. My head ached wickedly and I anticipated that as I had had a day off the after-dinner chores would be reserved for me.

If poor Bill needed any punishment for monopolising the arm-chair Mary had it in store for him.

"Why did you bring Atholl Williams here?" she asked him.

"I've brought lots of chaps here," said Bill airily. He looked around us as if conferring a great compliment. "You know, the chaps like coming here. You girls can always be depended upon to provide some entertainment." This last seemed to have some wicked meaning and he winked across the table at Evan. Mary caught the wink in passing. A slow flush mounted her face. Mary hated scenes. To the rest of us it was the meat and drink of life, but to Mary a scene was a shameful and indecent exposure. She knew just what Bill's words meant and how much passed between Bill and Evan when they exchanged winks. The flush in her cheek now was a danger signal.

Bill had his mouth full when he next spoke. That in itself was an affront to Mary.

"Atholl Williams is a pretty good bloke," he said. "I can get some useful material for the paper from him. His family have got diaries dating back to the first colonists."

"I suppose you think this place is a sifting ground for newspaper information," I said morosely.

Mother looked at me meaningly.

113

"Do you *have* to speak so rudely, Theodora?"

"She's got a headache," said Bill with Christian forgiveness.

"Theodora's not the only fish in the pond," said Denney. She was looking at the last serving on the dish and Mother, anticipating her request for more, kicked her under the table. Denney knew quite well why she was kicked, but she assumed innocence.

"Ouch! My ankle. What did you kick me for?"

Mother looked at her blandly.

"I was uncrossing my legs," she said. "Bill, let me give you another helping? I'm sure you're hungry after your long day."

Bill passed his plate and beamed on Mother. He might be out of favour with the girls but it didn't matter so long as Mrs. Monty was his champion.

"Don't bring Atholl Williams here again," said Mary doggedly.

Mother looked at her.

"I don't know why you've got such a set on that boy," she said. "He has very nice manners and he comes from a good family. What's more he's Vicky's friend. Why do you want to take Vicky's friend away from her?"

We all looked at Vicky. The red was stealing up her neck. There was a hint of tears in her eyes now. She was intensely nervous about Atholl Williams. She had been enchanted and disturbed by his sophistication, and a little bewildered by his interest.

Mary, however, knew all about Atholl Williams' type of sophistication. She was fiercely protecting Vicky in her banishment of Atholl Williams.

"He's not nice," she said flatly.

"What do you mean 'not nice'?" asked Denney. Bill and Evan exchanged meaning looks. The looks said that it wouldn't do any harm to disturb the virginal armour surrounding the pseudo-gregariousness of the Montgomery girls. Mary read the interchange of looks again and understood their message. Vicky, she was certain, had no weapons with which to withstand the spurious charm of Atholl Williams.

"Mother," Mary said flatly, "you're not to let Vicky go out with Atholl Williams. He's not to take her on the river in a boat, anyway."

"Why not?"

"She can't get out and walk home," I said.

Mother was perturbed. She wanted Vicky

to have her share of admirers, but she saw Mary's point.

"Since when have you given Mother orders about our friends?" demanded Denney.

"Mind your own business," said Mary.

"When I'm grown up properly," said Denney, "I'll bring who I like home, and Mary can keep her selfishness to herself."

Denney still hadn't won a retort from Mary and she was like a dog at a bone when she meant to torment someone.

"I suppose Atholl Williams hasn't even noticed that you exist," she said.

"I wouldn't want to exist for people like Atholl Williams," said Mary quietly. She paused a moment and then added with sudden anger. "Shut up, Denney! You don't know what you're talking about. Atholl Williams is no good for Vicky or anyone else in this family."

Mother looked at Mary. So very young and so early wise.

Denney's violet blue eyes fixed themselves with a deadly provocation on Mary. Her mouth twisted up sideways.

"We'll see about that," she said. "And we'll see how you'll stop *me* when I'm good and ready."

116

Denney was only rising sixteen, but she was wild enough to carry out her threat.

"I'll stop you," said Mary.

The blue eyes still looked insolently across the table.

"Just how?"

Mary had her cup of tea in her hand.

The colour drained from her face and she half-stood up. Denney saw her intention and pushing back her chair so that it fell over she dodged to the right.

In the act of throwing Mary's hand followed the course of Denney's dodge and before she could stop herself the contents of the cup had flown across the table—and had been intercepted by the one object that was now between Denney's dodging head and Mary's swerving hand—Mother's face.

There was a horrified silence round the table. Denney stood irresolute in the doorway, Bill and Evan put down their forks and stared. This was something unprecedented, even for the Montgomery girls. Mother sat still and silent, the warm brown tea flowing in little unchecked rivulets down her face, off her chin, on to her white silk blouse.

Then where the drips of tea had hung on

her lashes there now welled suddenly tragic tears.

We were all of us overcome. We remembered our relentless quarrelling. We sat mute, weighed down heavily by unutterable grief.

Vicky and Gerry moved first. As if by a common impulse they flew round the two sides of the table. Both wound their arms around Mother.

"Mummy darling!" and Gerry began to sob wildly. Vicky wiped the tea and the tears from Mother's face, she looked around at us with a quaint ill-fitting hauteur—

"Awful creatures!" she said with withering scorn.

"There speak the Bastons," I said furiously. I wished that we all were dead, that we had never been born.

Gerry had got herself on to Mother's knee and was cradling her head on the tea-soiled blouse.

Mary stood up quietly and began to clear the table. In silence I followed suit. Presently Mary went upstairs with Evan. Denney disappeared so Bill and I did the washing-up.

My head began to thud. I was wildly and furiously unhappy. I longed to comfort Mother, but her mockery of my moods had erected a wall of silence between us in matters of the heart. We could laugh with one another and against one another but there were no words that could express comfort or grief.

I heard Mother coming out of her moment of self-pity with characteristic robustness.

"Never mind, Gerry," she was saying. "They're sorry now. We can't help this quarrelling, but thank goodness it doesn't really mean anything. Underneath it all we stick together. That's the great thing. That's why we're so strong as a family. We stick together. Unity is strength!"

I gritted my teeth.

Gerry and Vicky went on hovering about Mother like a pair of angry virtuous Puritans.

"Anybody would think Gerry never did anything to make Mother unhappy," I said indignantly. "As for Vicky . . . whenever she's most needed she's down at the Bastons'."

"That's enough, Theodora," said Mother, coming into the kitchen. "Don't *you* start another quarrel. If your head is so bad you can't keep a civil tongue in your mouth, you can go to bed."

"How can I go to bed?" I said. "Mary and

Evan are holding hands on the balcony. On my bed too . . . I'll bet."

"Then get into Vicky's bed till Evan goes," Mother said quietly.

I undressed and had a bath and took myself up to the curtained part of the passage where Vicky had her bed. I was barely between the cooling sheets, my blazing head finding heaven in the soft pillow, when Vicky was standing beside me.

"Get out of my bed," she commanded.

I rolled over and showed her my back.

Vicky pranced to the head of the staircase.

"Mother, make Theodora get out of my bed. I *won't* have her in my sheets. I *won't* go to bed in sheets Theodora's been sleeping in."

For once Mother called Vicky to order.

"Come down here, dear," she said. "She really has a bad headache. I could see by the look in her eyes. I'll give you clean sheets when you go to bed."

Dash it all, wasn't I *clean*? I flung myself out of the bed, tore off the sheets and began to hang them over the doorways and balustrades of the staircase to air. The blankets I spread over the clothes-horse which I dragged from the bathroom: I sprayed the whole with antiseptic until the upstairs hall stank like the ante-room of a dentist's surgery. The place looked like somebody's nightmare drawing of a second-rate laundry.

I strode out on to the balcony and ordered Mary and Evan out of my sight.

My head on my own pillow I wept salt and bitter tears. In my ears there drummed Mother's war-cry—"*We'll always stick together!*"

"Never, never, never!" I cried. "Hateful family! If only I could be free! If only I could be *free*!"

2

JAKE

THE Teachers' College in Claremont was a rather noble affair, in a barn-like kind of a way. Its architecture was pretentious. It was a great stone building topped with castellated turrets. It was Tudor-cum-Georgian with a fine Norman door at its main entrance. Yet for all its oddity it was not without an inept and forlorn beauty.

I was, at first, a lone wolf, or better still, the cat who walked by herself when I first came to the College. Ninety per cent of the students came up in gangs from the principal State high schools. They spoke the same language and understood the same traditions.

Of the hundred and fifty students in the College only four of us came from the private secondary schools and each of us came from a different school. We each walked alone, bewildered by the alterations in academic standards and by the group behaviourism of the

122

great bulk of students. Those amongst them who had been their leaders in schooldays automatically became their leaders in student-college days. For them, we four didn't exist.

This state of affairs did not discourage me in any way. I was excited and stimulated by the course of studies, I was near the beloved river again, I was away from my crowded, quarrelling family, I was bewildered but intensely interested in the curious interplay of personality amongst the serried ranks of ex-high school students. In scholastic matters theirs was the jungle law. Not in any of them did I find curiosity or a tender love for any subject. There wasn't time. In the matter of studies they were like dogged beasts of burden—they pulled relentlessly against the clock—and when the traces were lifted about examination time, they reverted to primitive times and fought one another for high placing on the examination lists. They had no time to stand and stare, and to think was to waste time.

I envied them their solid background of factual information. I looked inward at my own gaps and bewailed the days of slothfulness. I did not realise that the haunting wind in the pines and the pungent smell of the dead leaves beneath the gum trees gave to me more than any rule of thumb knowledge could ever have satisfied.

Once every month I hit the earth hard when I had to go out into the schools and discover for myself the long drudgery, the dull repetition involved in the process of teaching the very young; the insurmountable obstacle of professional obstructionism.

I knew almost at once that I would hate class-teaching. But I was irrevocably committed to it as a career. For this Mother had slaved and waited when she might have sent me out to earn a living years before. It was too late to change my mind. It wasn't my mind, anyway, it was hers.

In the meantime I had two years of college life before me. Two years of higher education in which I had at last found my feet and two years of the inspirational drive provided in education by the Professor; and in literature and philosophy by the access to a large, if oddly jumbled and incomplete library. For the first time in my life I was in the presence of more books than I could hope to read in the time allotted.

At the conclusion of the first term I met the short dark man.

124

None of the friends who had come to the house had touched my heart. I had learned that a mere kiss didn't result in the getting of a baby, and though on occasions I had sought and willingly received a kiss from one or two of my friends, the act of kissing had killed all desire to repeat the experience. Sometimes I was perturbed by the thought that having been kissed by a young man I could no longer bear the sight of him.

At the end of the first term in College I went for the three weeks' vacation to the home of one of the girls, another lone wolf in College, in the grass-lands north of the Swan River.

With this girl, Anna Doran, I had formed an acquaintance that bordered on friendship. We were thrown together out of necessity, for much assignment work had to be done in pairs and we two girls, outsiders as far as the majority were concerned, automatically formed one.

Anna was a pretty girl with jet black curly hair and coal black eyes. She was exceedingly timid and her whole life was one long pre-occupation with her family's affairs. She bored me, yet withal I liked her. I was flattered by her liking for me and I was sorry for her homesickness and for these reasons I responded to her need for my help.

It was with some misgivings, however, I accepted her invitation to Yannanoo. I was afraid of being bored by Anna multiplied by seven, I was afraid to show my own gaucheness in farm matters before her family, and I was afraid that I, with my preoccupation with books, would bore them. Yet I didn't want to go home to "Forty-five" and the family.

Thus five o'clock on an early winter evening saw Anna and me on the north-eastern train, myself nervous and reluctant, Anna joyous. Four hours' uncomfortable travelling in an old fashioned train brought us to the railway-stop nearest our destination.

"This is it," said Anna. There were tears of joy and relief in her voice. Her homesickness showed itself now in all its pitiableness. She was half-eagerness to tumble out first herself and embrace the lonely little station, half-anxiety for fear its littleness should frighten me.

"It's only a small place," she said apologetically, although there was a proud ring of "home" in her voice. She need not have feared for me. There was an irresistible appeal for me in the dingy kerosene-lamplit station.

At a buffet girls were selling steaming cups of tea and hot pies; the station-master walked about dangling a storm-lamp; a half-dozen farm hands lounged around with the loam from the fields on their boots and in their hair. A big, fair woman with a broad smile was greeting Anna.

Over all hung the indefinable, nostalgic smell that belongs to the Australian bush. It called to my blood like a song that was never learned but always known.

I was happy. It all had a curious and immediate effect on me. Standing beneath the station lamp I felt as if I had arrived at something which basically belonged to me. The Irish in me was only a halting-chain. This bush station with all its bush people and bush sounds belonged to the fundamental me. It was Australian, and so was I.

"So this is your friend, Anna?"

Mrs. Doran was shaking hands with me. The lamplight fell full on the face now. It was a broad, powerful face. There was no softness in it, and yet there were hints of a rich if raw humour when she laughed in her husky masculine voice. She was as fair as Anna was dark.

I began to think as we went down the ramp and piled our cases into the back of the trap of the things Anna had told me about her family. She had told me so often and I had never listened.

Her father was dead. There were seven children and her mother had farmed the big property with Anna's two elder brothers. The older girls did their share too. When Anna had arrived at the school-leaving stage it was decided there were already too many women on the farm. They all thought it would be a wonderful thing if Anna taught the little school in the township. Their ambitions for Anna were somewhat frustrated by the fact that the State insisted on some training before anyone could take up a post in a school. The Dorans had resisted at first, for they could see no reason why Anna should improve her education any further just to teach the children of the farmhands. But the State was obdurate, and Anna went to college.

She wept now as we travelled slowly over the bumpy creek road to the homestead five miles away. The moment of ecstatic return was over, and Anna, forgetting me, was pouring her troubles, her fears and failures, her dreadful homesickness into her mother's ears.

"But what nonsense, Anna," Mrs. Doran said, sitting bolt upright in the trap and flicking the mare on the rump. "Other girls from the country go to college. It can't be as bad as that." Her voice was stubborn and insistent. Anna's held a tiny note of frenzy. I knew what that meant. In her heart she knew she was struggling with a will stronger than her own. She had entered battle where defeat was certain.

She ceased her pleading to tumble out of the trap and undo the gate.

"Isn't Anna any good at college?" she asked me sharply.

"She's homesick," I said.

"Then she must grow out of it."

Anna climbed back in the trap.

"I'm sorry, Theodora," she said. "I'm being a bit of a beast. It's just reaction to homecoming."

Mrs. Doran spoke to the horse.

"How does the horse see in the dark?" I asked. The road was terrific. Sometimes one side of the trap was up in the air and sometimes the other side.

"She doesn't. She knows the way by heart. Every hole and anthill. You could tie the reins and go to sleep and old Minnie would take you home . . . if it weren't for the gates, of course."

"I'll ask Jake," said Anna suddenly.

I felt Mrs. Doran stiffen beside me.

"Ask Jake what?" she said harshly.

"I'll ask Jake if I can stay on the farm."

"Nonsense," said Mrs. Doran. I couldn't see her but I felt her lips clamp together.

"If Jake says I can stay home, then I can," said Anna with sudden resolution.

"But he won't," said Mrs. Doran and gave her wheezy laugh.

"Who is Jake?" I asked, partly to relieve the tension between mother and daughter and partly for the sake of something to say.

"Jake is my eldest son," said Mrs. Doran. There was pride with a qualifying note in her voice.

"Jake's the manager of the farm," said Anna. "We all do what he says . . . because we haven't got a father."

"Jake and *I* are the managers. And you do what Jake and *I* say," said Mrs. Doran.

She was proud of Jake. He was indispensable to her, but she wasn't going to let Anna use him as a Court of Appeal.

I was thunderstruck with amazement at the prospect of seeing five girls and one young man doing what their eldest brother told them to do.

130

I wondered about Jake. A big hulking boss-
ing type, I thought. I visualised him in
riding-breeches with a stock-whip in his hand.

Anna closed the third gate and the trap
turned off the rough road on to a sandy track.
The trees were high about us and now and
then there was scrub close flanking the track.
Then Minnie slowed down to a walk and was
picking her way across the creek.

We came from between the trees and were
running at a spanking pace along a wire
fence. On the brow of a hill I could see the
dark huddled shadow of a big low-built
house, and the little yellow gleams of light
from its windows.

"You've got sheep in the home paddock,"
said Anna.

"Yes, Jake put them there today."

Anna asked about her sister.

"How long will Helen be away?"

"Three weeks," said Mrs. Doran. "Jake
said you can do the dairy while you're on
holidays."

Ah ha! Where was the "Jake and *I*" talk
now. Either Mother did, or agreed with what
Jake said too, or it paid dividends to leave
him the arbiter of all their fates.

There was a hail in the darkness and we

slowed down to pass under a great wattle tree, through a gate where I could see a young woman standing by the posts.

"Hallo, Anna!"

"Hallo, Bee!"

"I'll shut the gate!"

We swung round the side of the house—both sides we passed in the buggy had wide verandas—and came to a stop in the stable-yards.

The smell of the earth was strong about us and except for our own creaking fumbling noises there was the silence of great isolation all about. Above the stars shone like lamps, the cold mist curled about our ankles and somewhere in the creek a bull-frog croaked.

The girl who had been at the gates came round the side of the house.

"I'll take Minnie out," she said beginning to unbuckle the straps of the trap. "There's dinner in the oven for you."

The footsteps coming across the yard arrived in the stable-yard and another girl held a hurricane lamp high in Anna's face.

"My, my," she said. "Our baby Anna's home." Suddenly she put down the lamp and threw her arms round Anna. Anna began to cry again.

"That's enough of that," said Mrs. Doran sharply and yet not altogether unkindly. "You're forgetting Anna's friend."

The girl disentangled herself from Anna's arms and picking up the lamp held it high over her head so that its yellow light shone on my face. On hers too.

"Hallo," she said. "I'm glad Anna brought you. I'm Bessy, the head of the family."

"I thought Jake was," I said absurdly.

"Oh, Jake's the boss, all right," Bessy said. "I'm the eldest of the girls though. Anna's our baby."

"Eldest of the family too," said Bee, giving Bessy away with promptitude. "There's two of us older than Jake."

Shades of the quick and the dead! They were older than him and they did what he said. What sort of family was this I had struck?

"Come straight into the bathroom," Bessy said to me hospitably. "You'll need a wash-up."

We went through a vast dining-room into a long passage which I could see passed straight through the house from front to back. A big man came stumbling out of one of the rooms and stopped awkwardly when he saw us.

133

"This is Bill," said Bessy. "He's just in from yarding. He'll have late dinner with you."

Bill held out a huge hand and shook mine too strongly.

"Do!" he said with a husky voice.

"Hallo," I said. I felt awkward too.

"Come on," said Bessy. "This way." Bill ambled up the long noisy passage and Bessy and I paused in the bathroom doorway. She had pretty curly hair, as fair as Anna's was dark. The brother Bill was fair too. Bessy's face was fair-skinned and she was blue-eyed and she had a pleasant welcoming smile.

"The room on the left in the front is yours," Bessy said. "When you're ready come up to the sitting-room . . . top of the passage."

Just as I had finished changing my dress Anna came in. She was merry and excited again.

"Hurry up," she said. "I'm starving."

"You're glad you're home, aren't you?" I said, looking at her in the mirror. For the first time I began to look at her with really seeing eyes. Even in the half-dark I was impressed with her home and her people. There was something solid and enduring about them all.

We clattered up the passage and came into

the circle of light in the middle of the sitting-room.

Mrs. Doran was rubbing her hands in front of the fire. Bill, the big brother, was standing beside her and turned now as we came in the door. One girl, another dark one, slithered out to put our dinner on the table and Bee and Bessy looked up and smiled. It was a large comfortable "lived in" room. In the centre was a table with a large standard lamp providing the only light except that which came from the crackling fire.

Against this centre table stood an arm-chair with its back to the door. In this someone was sitting, his back to us. He began to untangle himself from the papers that spread all over his knees. I could see that his hair was very black, like Anna's. Then when he stood up and turned round I could see his face was immeasurably shy. His eyes, black and tired and a little oddly matched, looked at me anxiously.

"This is Jake," said Anna.

He leaned forward and shook my hand.

"Why!" I thought amazed. "Why, he's only a shy, short man."

I stared at him awkwardly.

"He's dark and kind and awfully nice," I thought.

3

A HEART IS GIVEN AWAY

THE first I knew of the new day in the Grasslands was when Anna came in bearing a tray with a pot of tea and a plate of hot new-made rolls.

"Oh, Anna," I said. "How long have you been up? Why didn't you wake me?"

"Two hours," she said. "I've been up since six. We're not so hard-hearted that we expect our visitors to keep farm hours. You have your breakfast in bed. It will be a good holiday for you and you'll be out of our way."

"Couldn't I help?"

She looked at me archly.

"Can you work a separator?"

"No, but I can learn."

"Yes . . . and we'd be all the morning separating," she scoffed. "I've done it already. You can come and help me clean up the dairy when you're up," she relented. ". . . and wash the separator. That's a stinking job."

The breakfast was the loveliest I'd ever

eaten. The smell of the new bread rolls was in my nostrils, and outside the window was the occasional bleat of sheep, and the swift gallop of a horseman going down the paddock. The air was fresh and sharp with the smell of young grass. I couldn't get out of bed quick enough.

"Where's everyone?" I asked.

"Bee's polishing the passage," she said. "Can't you hear her? One grunt to every rub. Bessy's in the kitchen and Janet's gone out with the boys. They've gone to bring in a head of cattle they left at the Ten-mile yesterday."

I looked at her with some disappointment. I wanted to see how everyone looked in the daylight.

"When will they be back?"

"Not till to-night."

"I would love to have gone."

"Can you ride?"

"No, but I can try."

Anna started to laugh.

"It needs something more than a novice to cut out cattle," she said. "Still, you can learn. We'll start you off on Minnie. You can ride her into town with me this afternoon when we go to get the mail."

"Whoopee!" I said.

The sun was high in a blue sky but a fitful wind from the north brought a warning of rain. The wide paddocks sprawled down to the creek and flowed away wide again to the western ridge of limestone country. All was green. The creek road was marked by a line of trees, tea-tree and gums till it came to Allanson's place.

I looked at the homestead. A great white, low-lying thing of brick and stone. It had been there since the beginning of white man's time in Western Australia. It was completely surrounded by a wide veranda over which vines were trellised. The whole aspect of the home and paddocks was one of security and careful well-being. This was not a rich farm—yet. But a very good one.

In the afternoon old Minnie, the sometime hack, and a nice sprightly little horse called Magpie were caught and saddled for Anna and me to ride to town.

Watching me get up on Minnie was like a preview at a star vaudeville turn for the Dorans. They were all excellent horsewomen and they took a shrewd delight in seeing the city girl so inept.

"Why, Theodora," said Mrs. Doran,

"Anna told us you were the smartest girl in college!"

"So I am," I said giving back as good as I got. "I can win any swimming race and I play A Grade hockey. I'm not going to let this old buggy horse beat me."

At last I was up. I sat erect and thumbed my nose to the gallery.

"Mind she doesn't buck," jeered Bessy. I wasn't afraid. The only trouble was to get her to go fast enough to give me a thrill.

When we returned three hours later we staged a moderate gallop up the rise from the creek to impress the gallery which had heard us arriving and come out on the veranda to assess results.

In the stable-yard I fell more than slid off Minnie and I could only roll instead of walk across the gravel yard to the side veranda. Bessy and Bee laughed with wicked glee at my bent back and writhing face, nevertheless they had pity on me and made me a hot bath. Bathed and changed for dinner I came out on the front veranda, a new-made woman in every degree. I was full of the strangest exhilaration. I had never felt so peaceful and so happy.

The Doran family had won me because

they seemed the antithesis of my own. Their jeering at one another was without animosity and there was no bitter edge to their words.

Anna came out on to the veranda.

"Have you had a good day?"

"Oh Anna, lovely! And I love this valley, and your home, and all your family."

I looked at her apologetically, for I was sorry that I had not bothered to look at her with seeing eyes before.

"Isn't it quiet after college?" she said going to the veranda rail and looking out over the darkening valley. "You can hear anything coming when it's miles away.

"Hear it?"

I shook my head.

"You're not used to the country. It's Jake and the others. They will be home in half an hour."

I listened with straining ears but could hear nothing but the rise of the first bull-frog and the lowing of a cow in the out paddock. I shivered slightly.

"It's getting cold," Anna said. "Come inside now. Bee's probably got the fire lit in the sitting-room."

We sat around the fire waiting, occasionally

talking, as one talks at the end of a good day, happily and gently.

Then Mrs. Doran lifted her head from her knitting.

"There's Jake now," she said. I noticed she didn't mention the others.

I could hear the light rhythmical stroke as the horses came at a gallop up the rise and rounded the house towards the stables.

"Anna, you go and see that Angus tends to the horses and then see if the bath is ready for the boys."

What about Janet's bath, I wondered.

No need to worry, for Janet had her bath first and came into the sitting-room, her hair wet and tousled, her face rosy. She had a pair of leather slippers in her hand. She put them in front of the fender. Mrs. Doran looked over her knitting and settled back in her chair as if everything had now been attended to. I wondered vaguely to whom the slippers belonged.

Bill came lumbering into the sitting-room. I noticed he had leather slippers on.

"Everything all right?" Mrs. Doran asked without looking up.

Bill grunted.

"'S going to rain," he said. "Dirty wind

coming up. Where's the papers? Any mail?"

"How did you know anyone went for the mail?" Bessy asked.

"Heard the horses going through Allan-son's. We were over the other side of the hills. Someone on Magpie?" He looked round quizzically.

"I was," said Anna. "You always know the way Magpie goes, don't you, Bill?"

He grunted again.

"Erratic as a grasshopper," he said, and began to open the papers.

I was waiting for Jake to come in. Would he have the same puzzling delighting effect on me as on the night before? Presently he came in in stocking feet.

He hesitated when he saw me and I thought for a moment he was embarrassed because he was without shoes. I watched fascinated as he went to the fender and stepped into his slippers. He looked round the room awkwardly. I was aware that for some reason everyone was looking at me.

What's wrong? I thought. I haven't said anything. Perhaps I should.

"Hallo, Jake," I said.

"Hallo, Theodora," he said.

142

He moved restlessly across the room and picked up a paper.

"Did Digger come home?" he asked his mother.

"No," she said without looking up.

"He's on the other side of the rabbit-proof fence if you ask me," said Bill from behind his paper.

"He'll go back to Baker's for the night if he can't get through the fence," said Bessy hopefully.

"Who's Digger?" I asked Anna.

"Jake's dog," she said.

Jake bent over the centre table and began to read his paper in the circle of the lamplight.

"Sit down, Jake," said Mrs. Doran.

Everyone was looking at me awkwardly.

Bill rustled his paper and then looked round the edge at me.

"You're sitting in Jake's chair," he said.

Hell, I thought. That's why everyone was looking at me.

"Oh, I'm sorry," I said. I jumped up and went across to the fireplace and sat on a small cushioned stool.

Jake flushed.

"It's all right," he said. "Please sit in the chair if you would like."

"Dinner will be ready in a minute," Mrs. Doran said flatly.

"I don't really want the chair," I said gravely. "I just didn't know it was yours."

Jake sat down apologetically. I looked at him. What did he have that they all treated him in this semi-god fashion? I was trying to read the riddle in his quiet composed face, in his slightly odd, dark, brooding eyes, in his square brow and the jet black hair that crowned his head like a cap. He looked up from his paper and our eyes met. He looked away quick and I turned my head and stared into the fire. He was immensely shy.

And they put his slippers on the fender! What about Bill's slippers?

I looked at Bill. He was nodding behind his paper and quite involuntarily he gave a loud snore. Everyone laughed.

"Wake up, mister," Mrs. Doran said. "Dinner's ready and you'll have to eat first."

"Jake," I said. I wanted to make him look at me again.

"What's that?" he said looking round the paper at me.

"I went for a ride this afternoon."

"Good for you!"

"I haven't ridden before," I said by way of explanation.

"Is that so?" he said thoughtfully. "I suppose you rode Minnie. You must try Berry to-morrow . . ." He paused for a long time as if debating some urgent and delicate matter. Everyone waited until he had finished what he was saying before we moved towards the door. "He's a thoroughbred but very well behaved."

We proceeded to the dining-room where Jake carved the joint methodically in a formal and considering manner. I was still determined Jake should take an interest in me.

"I trotted, I cantered, I galloped," I said doggedly. They all looked at me. There was something wary and brooding in their eyes. I was too young to realise that other girls had been here to Yannanoo before me.

"Good for you," said Jake thoughtfully. He began then, slowly and anxiously, to tell his mother of the head of cattle they had brought in from the Ten-mile that day. He spoke of his intentions regarding them, of market prices and the difficulties of immediate trucking at the railway siding. His remarks were tinged with the faintest melancholy and pessimism. I was to learn that farmers always talked thus on the eve of a "deal."

It seemed to me as if everyone hung upon his words. No one would have dreamed of interrupting, of initiating a discussion. I began to see that always it was Jake's judgment that was final; that support from Bill and Mrs. Doran was automatic because they had such complete faith in him; that Jake's explanations were not so much a matter of justification as a rational policy of keeping his family, who were his fellow shareholders, informed of his day-to-day moves in connection with their collective property.

I began to feel something in the nature of the holy respect for Jake. For all his quiet anxious manner he had the courage of his own authority and a great confidence in his own judgment. He showed his cards now as if in a game which was already over. Part of the power he had over the family lay in their intrinsic respect for that confidence and judgment, and their awareness of the responsibility he carried so justly, so unpretentiously, so consciously on his thin shoulders.

When dinner was over Jake went to the back veranda and shouted at Angus to know if Digger had come home. There was still no sign of the dog.

We sat round the fire and yarned. Bill went to sleep in a methodical kind of way that told me he did this every night. I kept stealing surreptitious glances at Jake.

For a while he read the papers, but presently I could see that though he was looking at a paper he was not reading it. It seemed to me as if he was listening for something outside the room.

At last he put the papers down and sat brooding into the fire. The wind was a mild gale now and the room was becoming uncomfortably warm.

"Rain," said Mrs. Doran. In her voice there was the heavy satisfaction of the farmer who knows that when water comes down from the skies in plentiful quantities and at the right time, it is raining banknotes.

Jake stirred restlessly.

"Digger'll go back to Baker's," said Bessy suddenly.

"He was pretty tired," said Jake. "He was the only dog we had on the cutting out. Baker's place is a good five miles from the rabbit-proof fence."

"How far is the rabbit-proof fence from here?" I asked.

"Five miles," Mrs. Doran said. She went on knitting, complacent, implacable.

"He's been in bad weather before," said Bill suddenly waking up. I guessed that though he went to sleep he knew everything that was going on.

Jake said nothing but rolled himself another cigarette.

About half past nine Jake went outside. Perhaps ten minutes later heavy footsteps crunched on the gravel path leading to the stables. Sometime after I heard the sound of a horse going fast downhill towards the creek. At the same time a gale of wind and sleet hit the house and played a drumming tune on the iron roof.

"Where's Jake gone?" I asked puzzled.

"He's gone to get Digger," said Mrs. Doran. She didn't look up from her knitting. She was unmoved and still complacent.

"He didn't say so," I said.

Nobody answered me for a moment, and then Bill stirred again, opened his eyes and yawned.

"He's gone to get Digger," he said with finality. "Who's going to get supper to-night?"

Anna looked at me.

"Shall we?"

I jumped up happily.

"Anna," I said, in the sanctuary of the kitchen. "Has Jake really gone back five miles to get his dog?"

"Of course," she said.

"Will he *see* well enough?" I asked. Clearing fences on a pitch-black stormy night!

"He'll see all right. Knows the way like the palm of his hand."

"Did he *have* to go?" I asked, awed.

"A cattle dog is a man's best friend. Jake wouldn't let Digger down."

We made toast and tea and then enjoyed it by the comfort of the fire while outside the rain storm swelled. No one mentioned Jake or the dog.

When I went to bed it was a long time before I could sleep.

Presently I fell asleep and it seemed long hours afterwards that I woke to the sound of a horse's hoofs pounding up the rise.

"Jake's home," I thought. I lay and listened.

By and by I heard him come down from the stables. I heard his step on the back veranda and then him moving about his room. Digger came round into the side veranda near my

149

window and I heard him scratch himself then throw his body on to the wooden floor of the veranda. The dog yawned and gave a long sigh. An iron bed creaked on the side veranda where the boys slept.

Outside the rain thundered on the roof. Inside all was still, and all were at peace.

4

THE LAST RIDE TOGETHER

THE rain passed over and the sun shone again on the valley. The days passed as gently and sweetly as the dew lying on the green rolling paddocks.

We went mushrooming; we rode across the hills; we walked in the rain when it came again at the end of the week, and we laughed and talked and were hilarious. I laughed at anything. Wildly and happily. I thought it was because of the peace that was in the low hills and the scent that was in the paper-barks in the creek bed.

But it was because of something stirring in my heart, unbidden and unrecognised.

At the end of the first week Jake said I might ride over the limestone ridge with him.

The wary look was in the eyes of the family again. Again I did not recognise it for the thing it was, and I paid no heed.

We made a joke and a game of bringing in a horse. Berry it was this time, I'd already outgrown Minnie. The girls screamed with laughter when I put on a red pullover.

"For goodness' sake," they cried. "Everyone in the countryside will laugh at Jake if they see him out with someone with that thing on."

"Mind the bull in the far paddock," Bessy jeered. "You won't have a hope with that red flag."

"You certainly mean to be seen," Mrs. Doran said.

I stuck to the pullover, though, because I knew red was becoming to my black hair and fair skin. I had red lips too.

They all gathered in the stable-yard to see us off. If Jake was taking a lady out they were making it a family concern. I made a joke of scrambling into the saddle because I didn't want to look idiotic. Better to laugh at myself, and very loudly, than give them the chance to do it quietly amongst themselves.

We went over the limestone, Jake leading, his silence round him like a cloak.

Half a mile up on the other side of the ridge we dismounted and I saw the reason for Jake's ride. Several sheep were almost neck deep in the mud round the edges of the dam.

"Always happens after the first rains," he

said. He got two by their heads and pulled them out. The third was too far gone. He took the gun from his saddle.

"Oh, no!" I said.

"You go up the hill," he said. "You needn't look."

Presently Jake came up on his horse. He looked down at me and for the first time I could see his dark eyes smiling at me. I could see now that they were slightly odd because the sight in one was not so good as in the other. He turned his head slightly and looked more out of one eye than the other.

"Softy, aren't you?" he said. "You'd never do on a farm."

"Oh yes, I would," I said. "I could learn."

He laughed as he rolled a cigarette.

"Do you want one?" he asked.

"Please," I said.

Our eyes met over the flaring match. What is it, I asked myself. What is this strange thing I read in his face? Is it really in his face or only in my eyes?

I felt happy but very shy. For once my tongue could find no words and the silence between us was stiff and awkward.

It seemed as if this was the moment, when we sat side by side on the hill and looked across the paddocks to where they flowed into immeasurable distances, that we could say so much. Surrounded by the family intimate conversation was impossible; the characters we wore then were but the trappings of artificial selves. And yet we were silent. Did Jake feel as I did? I didn't know. I never was to know.

When we finished smoking he looked at me again and his odd dark eyes smote me in the soft place that was my heart.

"Shall we be going?"

"Yes," I said. The moment was gone, lost, and never to be recovered.

When we came into the stable-yards he helped me down from the horse. His hand held mine and it was as hard as iron. For a moment we stood thus. It was dark in the stables and his hand was holding mine. The blood pounded in my throat and I was embarrassed so that I turned my head away and fiddled with my spare hand at the horse's stirrups. I didn't know what to say myself, but I longed for him to speak. Then I turned back and he dropped my hand.

"Hope you're not stiff," he said flatly, awkwardly.

154

"No," I said. "If I stay here long enough I'll be quite a good rider."

"I hope you do," he said as he began to unsaddle his horse.

"Thank you, Jake," I said gravely.

He didn't answer and then we heard Anna coming across the gravel yard.

He had made me a cigarette and he had held my hand.

That was all.

That night we sat round the fire. I sat on the floor and rolled cigarettes. First I made some for Bill, then I made some for Jake. Making Jake's cigarettes took a long time and I made them carefully. I licked them myself.

The next morning something flashed through my mind at the moment of waking.

The thing that had stirred in my heart no longer hurt. It soared like a bird. Like a lark it went straight to heaven.

I was the one who was wary now. When I went outside to join the others I was careful never to mention Jake's name. I was frightened to look them in the eyes for what they would read in mine.

Inside me the bird in my heart was singing, singing, singing.

"Let me cook the dinner," I asked Bee.

She scoffed.

"You couldn't cook a dinner for all of us. There's six men in the kitchen, don't forget."

"Of course I can cook a dinner," I said. "What do you take me for?"

"All right. If Jake says so you can cook the dinner."

"What on earth's it got to do with Jake who cooks the dinner? All he's got to do is eat it."

"It's the men in the kitchen," said Bee. "They've got to be fed and fed well. Jake's very particular about that."

"I give you my word of honour I'll give the men in the kitchen the best dinner they've ever had in their lives. But I won't have you ask Jake." I felt my jaw sticking out.

"All right," said Bee reluctantly.

She showed a tendency to hang around and supervise.

"Look," I said. "I'm doing this so you can have the afternoon to yourself. Now you buzz off."

She watched my quantities anxiously. I put the vegetable knife down and looked at her squarely.

"Well?" I said. "Any faults?"

She laughed.

156

"All right," she said. "I'll get out. Only God help you if there's not enough, or it's burnt, or anything like that. I'd never have the courage to face Jake."

"Oh, Jake be blowed!" I said.

I wasn't cheating myself, however. I was cooking Jake's dinner. I was as much a mug as the rest of them. I was waiting on him, serving him, and presently I would hang on his lips for words of approval just as they did. Even the humblest of them was not as subservient as I.

When I had had my bath I hung about the veranda waiting for the sound of a horseman. It seemed as if all my life I would remember that darkling valley with the silence of night descending upon it and myself waiting there, listening for the sound of Jake coming home.

Presently I heard his horse cantering up the hill. He passed up the paddock but did not turn his head or look towards the veranda. It seemed to me as if he was carved in the saddle. His hat was pulled down low over his eyes and he looked straight in front of him. When he had gone round to the stables I went inside.

I waited for him thus every night. I waited all day and for that one sound, the beat of the horse's feet bringing Jake home. It made a music in my heart that has never been quite forgotten.

After that, nothing happened. Nothing at all.

The family closed ranks. I could see the certainty of victory in their eyes.

This had all happened before.

They would do practically anything on earth for Jake but they wouldn't let any woman get him.

I could see the implacability writ large through Mrs. Doran's character. She didn't fire any bullets. I don't think she even made any. She let the girls do all that, with her full knowledge and approval. If they had failed, only then would she have taken up the fight. And her greatest ally was Jake's inherent shyness.

Jake didn't ask me to go riding again. I don't know why. I used to think it was because they ragged too much about it and his shyness defeated him. Perhaps he didn't even want to take me!

But it would have been an utter impossibility for Jake to rise from his chair, cast aside his many papers and say—

"Come Theodora, let's have a walk by the creek in the moonlight."

It is something neither he nor I could have achieved beneath the watching protective eye of that family. And if we had achieved it, it would have meant only one thing. And who, under such short notice with so little real knowledge of the workings of the human heart, of the waywardness of Theodora Montgomery, could have taken so irrevocable a step?

And who would have dreamed that such an inexplicable thing as shyness would so wall and hedge Theodora that she could make no gesture? Besides, she was afraid of the invincibility of that family.

Also she was very young and very foolish. She didn't really know the game in spite of her assumed sophistication.

To begin with the Dorans teased unmercifully. Not about Jake, of course, but about the wild hilarious time we city people had in Perth. About what poor country bumpkins they and their men appeared by comparison. They teased about the flirtations they were certain were a constant and titillating part of my life. They teased about the dances, balls, parties to which they were certain I went. They teased about boyfriends.

And I played back. I gave as good as I got.

159

Without realising what was happening I found myself in the role of sophisticated party-girl. I found myself a know-all.

I was drawn into literary discussions and before I knew where I was I was laying down the law about poetry and writers. I became my father's child.

Then they would all gaily announce they never read a book anyway and what had being a high-brow to do with the business of providing bread and butter for the nation? All city people were parasites on the farmers.

"Shakespeare this . . . Shakespeare that . . ." said Bill sententiously. "What did Shakespeare know about a farm? That's the crux of the matter. How could anyone live, let alone write books and poetry. . . . POETRY mind you . . . if somewhere the farmers weren't feeding and clothing him?"

Jake put down his paper slowly. Everyone waited for the pearls that would drop from his lips.

"Sir James Mitchell, now he is the greatest Statesman. . . ." We waited while he thought what he would add next. Jake corrected himself. "The ONLY Statesman this State has known. . . ."

I was young and fevered with the argument. I could not wait as the others did.

"What about Lord Forest?" I demanded. "He brought us into Federation."

"FEDERATION!"

"Federation! Coal-miners and lumpers of the Eastern States battening on the farmers of Western Australia!"

"Federation! The worse thing that ever happened to Australia."

"Federation! Why don't they mind their own business, over there. We're all for secession. Why should they lay down laws to govern people fifteen hundred miles away and whose existence they don't care a fig for."

"Stuff and nonsense," I said. "Why don't you read a book on Economics. Or even one on National Defence."

I went to bed and wept because I couldn't hold my tongue. They'd let me show myself up as the "outsider"; the frivolous city type who was prepared to sell the State into the bondage of the Men at Canberra. And I'd done it all myself.

They weren't country bumpkins.

They were strategists of the highest calibre.

5

BACK TO COLLEGE

AT the end of three weeks' holiday Anna came back with me to College. A few days earlier she had been closeted for half the afternoon with her mother and Jake in the tiny ill-lit study where Jake conducted the business side of running a big property. Anna emerged with her eyes swollen from weeping but with a gleam of hope brightening their darkness. There was a special bond between Anna and Jake. I had thought all along he wouldn't be hard on her.

Between them all they had decided that Anna's chief unhappiness lay in her homesickness. She was to give College one more try. The day following the interview she showed me a cheque Jake had given her for extra pocket-money.

"I'm not to tell the others," she said conspiratorially. "It's not out of the estate. It's his own money."

"Jake's got money of his own?" I asked

idly. There was no satisfying the hunger of my heart for every detail of his way of living.

"Oh, yes, quite a lot. Our uncle left nearly everything he had to Jake."

I began to see something of the reason for the Dorans' guard. Maybe they thought every woman who looked at Jake with soft eyes was a fortune hunter. I couldn't have cared less about his money. I sought only for a glance, a softening of those black eyes so like Anna's and Janet's yet with the oddness in them.

Anna and I drove along the creek road in the gathering dusk on our way to catch the train. Mrs. Doran held the reins and Anna chattered endlessly. Occasionally, her mother put in a word but I sat silent, watching the thin spectre of the ring-barked trees as they slid past on Allanson's place. My thoughts were with one moment just before we had gone out to the stables.

Jake had stood in the passage and rolled me a cigarette. His eyes had been on it as I thanked him for having me. He finished rolling the cigarette, licked it down, folded the ends in with a match and then gave it to me. Our eyes met a minute. I tried to put apology for my rambling argumentative tongue into mine.

Both our fingers lingered on the cigarette. His eyes were dark and suddenly desperately inarticulate. I knew they tried to say something.

Then Bee came out into the passage.

Jake shook hands with me and I turned away.

A frustrated moment. And yet was it really? My heart clung crazily to the tiny gesture. Yet it could not inspire grace in my limbs nor the right smiles on my lips at this moment.

Probably there was never anything in it, yet for one moment I had thought . . .!

Back at College I fed and nourished the friendship with Anna.

The endless chatter about her relatives was now meat and drink to me. Every time I looked at her black hair and dark velvet eyes I thought of her brother. Moreover, I wanted to be asked to Yannanoo again.

I took her home to "Forty-five" for an occasional weekend and for half-holidays, and after overcoming her first attack of shyness she blossomed under the cross-fire of Montgomery tongues.

"Theodora seems to have been a different person since her holiday," Mother said.

"What did you do to her up there in the country?"

"Oh, we went riding, and walking," said Anna. "I think it was just the Grasslands' air."

"Country air, pooh!" said Denney. "She was up to something more than breathing in ozone and grass seeds. Look at the life she's led Bill Jennings ever since she's been back. How many men have you got up there?"

"I've got two brothers," Anna said doubtfully.

"Cherchez l'homme," said Denney.

Denney gazed at me with big insolent violet eyes. I dared her to say another word. Mother came to my rescue.

"Denney, if you must be vulgar keep it for a private family session."

"Ho, ho!" said Denney. She began to suck an orange noisily. But I was getting longer in the tooth and I knew two of that. I took a big hard apple and bit off large pieces and ate them with my mouth slightly open. They crunched beautifully.

"I'm mad about your family," Anna said enthusiastically as we caught a late bus back to College. "Aren't they interesting? And isn't Vicky lovely? Just like a china doll. And

165

as for Denney . . . why she's beautiful! If I could be tall and willowy and have blue eyes and arched brows like that. . . ."

"What about Mary?" I said. "Lots of people like Mary the best."

"Yes. I do too," Anna said soberly. "She's very sweet, and she has those huge 'talking' eyes. I think I do like her the best. Only it's hard to think about the rest of you when Denney and Gerry are in the room. They're so funny. And witty, in a clever way."

"All very amusing, if you don't have to live with them," I said sourly.

"Well, at least you'd never be bored," Anna said. "And what about that wonderful mother of yours. . . ."

"Yes," I conceded that. "She is wonderful. And no one will ever really know how wonderful."

The next morning I saw Paul Denton standing on the steps outside the Norman door at College.

He was tall and he was golden and the sun shone on his hair until it was like burnished gold.

His clothes were immaculate, his bearing assured without being arrogant, his manner

166

aloof yet with a certain possibility of merry charm. His profile was better than John Barrymore's and his eyes were golden brown and intelligent.

All the girls looked at him.

So did Theodora Montgomery.

I came down the main staircase to look at the mail-table when I first saw him. And I stopped and stared. He looked up and I expect some of my thought must have been in my face because his brown eyes smuggled an illicit smile my way, and I made no odds about smiling back.

I went into the education lecture and squeezed past a dozen students to where Anna was keeping my place.

Presently Professor Angus came in and I could see by the look on his face we were in for a good lecture.

He was a tall, thin man with sharp grey eyes that missed nothing. Now and again he dropped heavy witticisms at the expense of the heads bowed over the notebooks, but the pens scratched ruthlessly on.

Later, with surprise and acute interest, I viewed a certain golden head as it appeared over the crowd in the dining-room. And its owner was seated amongst the students! What was this? Clearly he no more belonged in this stable than might the gifted and beautiful son of a millionaire.

That, by our standards, was pretty much what Paul Denton turned out to be.

He was the son of a large and wealthy land-owner. Being a young man with a will of his own, and having had a major row with his progenitors, he had been literally, if temporarily, thrown out of the soft-lined nest and had found his way to the only institution of higher learning, other than the gaol, where the Government and not the parents kept and fed as well as educated the inmates.

It would be unfair to say that entering the Teachers' College, because the education was at Government expense, was sheer opportunism on his part. He had more than a genuine flair for the academic life, he had strong views about the education of the young.

Whatever the causes of Paul Denton's admission, the results were highly beneficial. Apart from the fact that he lent grace and distinction to the College life he had the temerity to be "different" in his opinions, and the intellectual ability to justify his "difference." He had a really profound and well-explored knowledge of the great philosophers and writers of all ages. The real paradox of his presence in the College compared with other students lay in the fact that here amongst the educators was a person with real education as his background.

The women, who were in a two to one majority amongst the students, literally and unaffectedly fluttered their eyelids. Nothing quite so beautiful had ever appeared in their lives before. And oddly, the men liked him. In spite of his obvious and devastating appeal to the female, Paul was a man's man. He liked being with the men, talking to them. He excelled at some of the more masculine sports such as throwing the discus and long-distance running. And his conversation and erudition had certain male appeal to the mentally hungry men students. He was more jealous of these things too than he was over his easy conquests with women.

Paul and I became good friends almost at once. The first and most noticeable reaction of the College to our friendship was to strike the women nicely with envy and to raise my status all round with both the men students and the staff. They all put another interpretation on our relationship, but since even that added to my prestige I didn't mind. I had a good time that term.

Professor Angus, of course, took a special delight in the newcomer. He and Paul debated furiously, and in spite of Paul's gilded beauty Professor Angus liked him for his lucidity of thought and his knowledgeable individualism.

But Professor Angus always got the better of him in wit.

We were given several days' warning of our half-term examination in education.

"You will be given a single question," Professor Angus told us. "You will be asked to write a critical essay on any subject you elect provided it is related to modern educational methods."

Paul rose serenely from his seat.

"Have I your permission, Professor, to write a complete criticism of this institution?"

Professor Angus flashed back.

"No, you haven't. Don't be a fool. You've only got three hours."

One of the most attractive aspects of Paul's education was his knowledge of music. But mostly he was a student of poetry.

We walked and talked and argued. He was

brutal in his opinions of my level of intelligence and sometimes I sulked. But I always came back for more.

"Don't you realise that Browning as a poet appeals only to the adolescent ignoramus?" he begged angrily. "Your vanity is titillated by his classical allusion. You think you've got somewhere academically when you can see through his obscurities. You confound obscurity with depth. The finest poetry is never so involved.

"As a matter of fact, your mind fairly stinks with the rubbish poked away in corners. My God, Theodora, where did you collect so many worthless ideas? I estimate you'll be forty before you even begin to discriminate between the worthwhile and the worthless."

"I prefer Browning," I said obstinately.

"A servile mind," said Paul loftily of me.

"Rewarded well with servile punishment," I added angrily. In intellectual argument Paul treated me like the farm-hands on his mother's property. Presently he would recover himself and would begin to discourse at great length on poetry and poets. It was grand listening and I forgave him his boorish opinions of me. However, sooner or later and inevitably, I would barge in with some contribution of my own. He would stop dead in the moonlight . . . for, of course, we walked in the moonlight, the proper time for discussing poets in one's late adolescent years . . .

"Theodora," he would say piteously. "Once there was a garden. A beautiful cultivated garden. There came a beautiful lady, and fool-like, the gardener let her in. Of course she saw the *big* flowers. The tall poppies and the sunflowers. Her praise of them was extravagant. But not once would she look beneath her feet. Not even once, for beneath her feet lay trampled all the real beauties of the garden. The treasured simple things, the lovely modest things."

And here his voice would rise.

"She trampled in his garden!"

"So that's what you think I am . . . a trampler!"

"My God, I never knew a worse one."

Amongst Paul's friends was an Irishman, Paddy Donoghue. Often Paddy came with us on these walks and it was only he who saved me from utter annihilation when Paul really started on me.

"This about the garden, Paddy?" I said to him. "Am I such a trampler?"

"Moderately so, darrlin'," he would say. "But the lady who came a-visiting had such a beautful face, Theodora! You don't suppose any fool gardener would be looking at what her feet were doing!"

At home at "Forty-five" Paul was a kindred soul to the Montgomerys. They adored him at the piano, they fought vociferously with him on all subjects ranging from poets to politicians and from relics of colonial history to religion. They were amazed at Theodora's new conquest and they thought of us only in terms of the amorous.

"I can't think how Theodora got such a bad cold," Mother said one night. "Usually she plays too much hockey to get run down."

"It's not the hockey, it's the arundinaccous places," said Paul airily.

"Arundinaceous places? In the name of goodness what's that mean?"

"The reedy places. That's where we go at night-time. The reeds down by the river." Paul began to sing:

"Down by the river, summer nights I lie,
Stones for my pillow, and for roof the sky."

Mother looked at me sharply and I tossed my head.

"Oh, my, my!" said Denney. "What's our Theodora up to now?"

"We take Paddy with us," said Paul over his shoulder. "You needn't ask me my designs . . . or even my intentions."

He was playing "Fiddle and I" softly on the piano.

"Who is Paddy?" Mary asked looking up from her endless book of reference.

"Paddy is my darling . . ." sang Paul. Then he looked over his shoulder. "Ask Theodora," he said.

"The wild Irishman of College," I said morosely.

"My hat, haven't there been enough of the Irish in our lives without you walking out with one?" said Gerry.

"An Irishman!" said the others and dismissed him with a gesture. That settled Paddy's hash with the Montgomerys.

But he was a darling for all that. He had a thick mop of fair curly hair, the map of Ireland all over his face and blue eyes that disappeared between two slits when he laughed. And he laughed all the time.

We were an odd trio. Paddy was rough,

tough and, in comparison with Paul, nearly illiterate. A year of Paul's friendship, however, educated him. College never turned out a more successful teacher of music in the schools than Paddy. No one but God gave him his understanding of the human heart, his love for little hurt things, his rollicking laughter, his passion for lyrical music. But Paul taught him musical forms and modern harmony. Till then he had merely been nature's musician.

When Paddy left his class at the Practice School to which we were all occasionally posted for practical work, the children streamed after him. There was a music in his heart and it was as merry as a piper's. Everyone loved Paddy Donoghue.

The three of us walked the lanes. We lay on the yellow shores of the beach or we huddled in the arundinaceous places when we should have been at roll-call. Paul and I argued and Paddy laughed . . . and life was very good.

But I had not forgotten Jake. I dreamed of the dark horseman in the Grasslands, of the thud of horse hoofs bringing him home at sundown, of a face that was gentle and kind and inexplicably dear to me.

175

6

THE COMING OF SAM

SAM ought to be introduced with a flourish of fine writing. There should be some "approach", some delicate hinting that here comes one destined to be a major character in this story.

When I look back I remember that all the good qualities I now know in Sam we all knew in those College days. Yet we did not pause and think, and our eyes did not widen with the astonishing knowledge that here in our midst was a man of absolute integrity and spiritual courage.

I have no doubt at all that we all knew these things. I have a sneaking feeling that we probably thought, if we thought at all, that there were lots of other Sams in the world, lots and lots of good, wise people. We were very young and very callow.

The plain truth of it is that Sam did not come into our lives trumpeted by an escort of angels. For a long time he was simply a part of the scheme of things and though we were agreeably pleased at his presence, we took no great notice of him. So Sam came quietly amongst us.

He was Tutor in Education at the College. The students liked him and he was a centre of quite a coterie of the more serious-minded. He had a grave preoccupied air for one who was still very young. He had only passed through the College four years before our time. He brought with him the aroma of University bookishness and his academic reputation was formidable in spite of his youth. He had a string of high calibre degrees after his name but we bore with this because he was essentially human.

He was a tall young man with a pleasant though scholarly face. His best features were his eyes and he had long thick eyelashes which made the girls nudge one another. Sam took great pains to cover his eyelashes with pince-nez. He had a pleasant mouth which would sometimes relax into an unexpectedly boyish smile. He was what we called a "gum-nut" this being the college colloquial for a "swot" or genuine lover of books.

Added to these pleasing aspects of Sam Richardson was the teasing tit-bit of gossip

177

that he was a Quaker and at the same time it was whispered that even Quakers go through a period of "oat sowing." Sam, it was said, had a night-life. Nobody quite knew what it was, but it was supposed it had something to do with the members of the University Boat Club. They were looked upon as a wholly desirable but pretty fast lot.

The only one who didn't think much of Sam was Paddy.

"He's stuffy," Paddy said. "Ought to be shut up in a library with the moths."

But he had a kind heart where hungry students were concerned. I went to his study one evening with a late-finished tutorial and Sam was just about to pour his coffee.

"Sit down," he said. "I'll read your tutorial now while you drink your coffee."

I wanted the coffee and I liked the idea of sitting in the arm-chair in the fire-warmed study and talking to him. But I felt embarrassed about having my tutorial read in my own presence.

"Couldn't you leave that till to-morrow?" I begged him.

He looked up. I had a feeling that Sam missed nothing at all when he started looking at a person or a thing in earnest.

"They're not so good, are they?" I said, meaning the tutorials.

"If you think that yourself why do you hand them in?"

"It's no good trying to explain myself to you," I said sadly. "You're too logical. If it's not good, then make it better . . . that's your theme, isn't it? For me, I just know when I've done my best and maybe I still don't think it's so good."

Sam looked interested and slightly puzzled.

"It's an attitude not easy to understand," he said slowly.

I nodded.

"It's the Irish in me," I said. "The rotten streak."

He smiled.

"Have you read a book called *The Experiences of an Irish R.M.*?"

I nodded.

"Do Irish people really behave like that in Ireland?" he asked.

"I haven't been there," I said. "But if the rest of the nation is anything like my father and his friends I should say they do." I looked at him glumly. "That book's supposed to be amusing, you know," I added.

He nodded. His face still puzzled.

"Painful if you have to live with them," I said.

This time he really smiled.

All the same I felt that being Irish was no help in getting on with Sam.

Most of the time he gave me a feeling of being a worthless baggage myself. My attack on scholasticism was too flipperty-gibbet. The friendship between Paul, Paddy and myself, with Anna hovering rather pathetically on the fringes he thought was decidedly suspect. We had the earmarks of being pseudo-intellectual, the *bête noir* of the real scholar. Or so I feared.

However, we were too busy setting the world to rights, discovering music and great books and arguing about them to bother very much about Sam. Or anything else for that matter.

Then one day I was jerked out of my selfish preoccupation with Paul and Paddy . . . and I remembered Anna.

7

ANNA

THE term was drawing to a close.

Anna had been working feverishly. Had I given her half the care I should have done I would have seen she was arriving at a nervous pitch that was bordering on the serious.

With the approaching end of term, there loomed the hateful period in which we went out into the practice schools and had to take over classes from experienced teachers and put our learning to the practical test.

Upon these practical performances hung the certificate with which we ultimately hoped to leave College. This knowledge alone strung the nerves to concert pitch but to have to stage and sustain this performance under watchful and critical eyes was an ordeal that few if any could face with equanimity. Paul and Paddy were two of the exceptions.

Poor Anna began to show signs of frayed nerves a week before she had to go into a

181

school. I realised now what she was going through and I forgot a good deal of my own nervousness in a bullying attempt to encourage her.

The ends of Anna's fingers were blue and she shivered and a look of misery haunted the darkness of her eyes so that one moment I could cry for her and the next shake her.

Paul had no such terrors. He longed for the moment when he would stand in full academic battle-array before a class of senior high-calibre students. He would show them something. And he could, and would, and did. Paddy, too, had no nerves. He didn't care a damn for the tute or the school staff anyway. He and the children would have a good time. The head teacher would probably come in to see what the noise was about and stay to have a good laugh himself.

I once saw Paddy give a lesson and I put my head down on the desk and laughed till the tears ran down my cheeks. No tutorial class could ever discuss Paddy Donoghue's lessons afterwards. We'd all start to laugh again.

The fateful first day of "Practice" came and I was so busy facing my own ordeal that I could only spare fleeting moments to worry about Anna.

When half past three struck I walked over to the infants' school where Anna was posted and met her, drooping and white, in the doorway.

"Well, you're through all right," I said. "You're alive, aren't you?"

"Yes," she said miserably. "I scraped through."

"Who was your tute?"

"Miss Wright."

"A bit of a snorter. Still if you're alive after an ordeal with her you're all right. You'll be a hundred per cent to-morrow."

She walked beside me, silent and miserable. I felt suddenly angry with all those happy contented Dorans up there in the Grasslands. What did they mean by putting Anna through this? How little they could really know their sister, or the terrifying baptism of fire that learning to become a teacher involved.

"Buck up," I said again. "The worst's over."

"I wonder why Miss Wright didn't speak to me," she said heavily.

"Didn't she tell you how you got on?"

"No. She didn't say anything. She just wrote in my book all the time."

"Well, it couldn't have been anything bad. She would have told you."

It was a quarter of an hour before the school dinner bell the next day that a student came over from the infants' school and asked for me.

"The head teacher thinks you had better come," she said. "We told her you were Anna's friend. Anna's having hysterics."

I was shaken with anger. I'd seen this sort of thing happen before and knew what it meant. Anna had broken down in front of a class. Sometimes students got over it again, but I knew that Anna wouldn't.

As I hurried across the playgrounds I was filled not only with pity for Anna, rage against her tormentors, but a real sorrow that I had not been as good a friend as I might have been. I was heavy-hearted with remorse.

Anna was sitting on the lounge in the teachers' room. Her hair was disarranged so that it was a black fuzz above her head. Her face was buried in her arms and her whole body was wracked with uncontrollable sobs. The head teacher, a thin, stern woman, was sitting in a chair watching her. Plainly,

184

hysterical students bored her. She did not know which of them did it for effect and which from instability. I went straight in and sat down by Anna and put my arm around her. This increased the headmistress's irritation.

"I don't think that's the right treatment," she said. "These emotional girls must learn to stand on their own feet. They shouldn't be petted when they let themselves get out of control."

It was a strain to speak in the required tones of courtesy.

"She's not emotional, she's really the opposite by nature. This is not hysteria, it's plain breakdown from overwork."

"Since you're here you can take care of her. When she's ready you had better take her back to College. I expect Miss Wright will know what to do about her." She felt the scene was awkward and indelicate and she wished she didn't have to have the students about at all. She went out of the room and I sat on beside Anna. I said nothing but pulled her head down on my shoulder.

Her books were scattered partly on a chair, and partly where they had fallen to the floor. Topmost on the chair was that iniquitous instrument of torture, the black-covered, leather-bound Criticism Book. The thing the tutes wrote their remarks in. I picked it up and looked at Miss Wright's lengthy report on Anna's performance the day before. I began to read.

Oh, the cruelty of it! Not one redeeming feature was there recorded to recompense for the labour of weeks. No comments about the charts and illustrations which really were of an exceptional standard. Anna had no class personality. Her handling of the children was weak, her matter was without interest, her discipline bad, her voice squeaky and lacked command. It all went on for two pages.

When had Anna seen it?

I stood up and went into the hall and searched the notice-board to see in which classroom Anna had been posted. It was First Standard room 7. I went straight to the teacher.

"I'm Anna Doran's friend," I said. "Would you please tell me when Anna got her Criticism Book back from Miss Wright?"

My hands were clammy. I was afraid she would think I was impertinent and I only hoped she would understand my pity and concern for Anna.

"It was on the table this morning," she said. "I suppose Miss Doran read it when she first came in."

"And then she had to give a demonstration lesson in front of you?"

"Yes, I'm afraid so. Also the headmistress and Miss Wright from the College."

I gasped. I could feel the lump in my throat. I could see the soft look in the teacher's eyes and I knew she understood.

"How far did she get before she broke down?"

"About half-way through. I could feel it coming and I made an attempt to take the class over from her, but Miss Wright insisted on Miss Doran going on. She believes that these intensely nervous girls should master their nerves."

"But surely this was different?" I pleaded. "Anna was over-worked. She was worn out. And to give a demonstration lesson immediately after reading that Criticism Book! She must have felt Miss Wright had brought the headmistress in to confirm her own opinion of Anna's inability."

The teacher nodded. "Rightly or wrongly, she probably thought that. However, I'll tell you what I will do. I will ask permission to leave Miss Doran alone with the class for a few days. That will give her a chance to know the children and to get her confidence back."

I shook my head dolefully, for I felt that Anna's breakdown would be no passing thing. The teacher was young and, I suppose, remembered her own student days, for her eyes were full of regret.

"I wish I'd thought to hide that book until after her lesson," she said.

"Miss Wright is Tutor in Educational Psychology," I said bitterly.

I thanked her for her kindness and went back to the teachers' room and collected Anna's books.

"Come on, Anna. The bell's gone and we've got to get out of here. You don't want to meet the other teachers and students."

I half-pulled and half-pushed her out of the school. The sobs had stopped now, but she shook like a leaf as we walked up the hill and I had to help her.

I helped her back to College and up to her room. Matron began the same story as the headmistress of the school.

"Anna's ill," I implored. "This is not just nerves. It's breakdown. She's been working too hard for too long."

"We'll see about that," the matron said not unkindly. "Leave her to me now and I'll get her some tea and a hot-water bottle. That's the best thing I know for the shakes."

I went downstairs to Miss Wright's study. I knew I was faintly belligerent and I hadn't any real idea why I was going to her or what I hoped to gain in Anna's favour. Reflection would have told me that Miss Wright would consider my intrusion an impertinence, but in a sense I was fighting mad and even if I didn't dare openly attack Anna's enemy some compulsion in me sent me to face her.

"Well, how's Miss Doran?" Miss Wright asked briskly.

It was my turn to shake. I kept my eyes downcast for I knew I must not show this big-bosomed, self-assured, cold woman my sudden hatred for her. She had smiled at me suspiciously as much as to say . . . "here's one more of them."

"Anna's ill," I said. I began anxiously rubbing the knuckles of one hand with the other.

"I know Anna very well," I blurted out. "I've been in her home. It's different from the homes all these other students come from. She's never had to fight before. She's never been in competition before."

189

The persistent coldness of Miss Wright's eye eventually brought my stream of words to an end. I faltered and stopped.

"What *is* all this about, Miss Montgomery?"

"The Criticism Book. . . ."

"Whose Criticism Book?"

"Anna Doran's. She read it before she gave that lesson this morning."

"Would you mind telling me what Anna Doran's Criticism Book has got to do with you?"

"Anna is my friend." I bit my lips and stared out of the window. One cannot stare back a tutor but I was young enough to think I would be a moral coward not to have held my ground.

"Are you by any chance criticising me?"

"No . . ." I said miserably. "I only wanted to put in a word for Anna."

"I suggest you put it in with the Principal."

She had risen. The interview was at an end and I was to be reported to the Principal. For impertinence, I supposed. Basically I knew the Principal would forgive me and therefore I was taking an unfair advantage of a tutor in going thus to her. My action was not as brave as it seemed and because of this, and for this reason alone, I was later ashamed. Other tutors did not rule by tyranny and other tutors were just as successful as Miss Wright.

I was as nervous as a cat when the secretary gave me the word to go into the study. I was really worked up on Anna's behalf, and though I didn't care what Miss Wright thought of me, I didn't want to lose stature in Professor Angus's eyes.

"Come in, Miss Montgomery, sit down in that chair."

His reticent dignity smote me to the heart and punished me more than all Miss Wright's baleful stares.

"I want to know about Miss Doran," he said. "Tell me about her first. She is the more important person at the moment."

I told him about Anna. I told him of her work, of the family she came from, of her reasons for coming to College and of her promise to her brother. Then I realised I had been talking ceaselessly and he had been listening silently while the hands of the clock had moved relentlessly on. I stopped suddenly. Why was he looking at me like this? Was he summing me up by my account of

Anna and her life? Or was he thinking of Anna?

"Tell me, Miss Montgomery," he said. "You are a considerable protagonist in favour of Miss Doran, but do you think a person so hating the life and fearing the work should become a teacher? Isn't being a teacher a trust?"

"But Anna could be a good teacher," I said earnestly. "She's soft and feminine and maternal. It isn't *teaching* . . . it's the College, and its terrific pace; and the competition. Some people can teach wonderfully . . . but not in front of other people."

"What category do you fit yourself into, Miss Montgomery?"

"I can give a good lesson in front of people—" I hesitated a moment. "I show off a bit, you know," I said. "It helps."

A small smile hovered round the corners of his mouth.

"I'll never be a really good teacher," I said regretfully. "I can't bear the iron-bound curriculum. I dread the routine. I'm intimidated by the machine-like efficiency of all those teachers we meet in the schools. And I don't want to get like them."

192

"Do you think you should go on with the profession?"

"What can I do?"

I told him of my own family needs, of the sheer economic inability to set about, at my age, training for some other work.

"My mother set her heart on it," I said helplessly.

"I see," Professor Angus said after a minute. "A great many students find out too late they really do not care for the work. And they haven't the means to change their profession. Nevertheless, they are in a position of trust and must not allow the children to suffer for their mistakes. And now about Miss Doran. I shouldn't be surprised if she succeeded where you fail."

"I haven't failed yet," I said.

His mood changed and he seemed to come to life.

"So that's put you on your mettle has it? Now where is this place in the Grasslands?"

"Yannanoo."

He looked down a long list that he took from a wire basket on his desk.

"Yannanoo has a vacancy for a monitor next term. I propose to recommend Miss Doran for that vacancy. She'll get some teaching experience as a monitor, though the salary is very low. If after a year she likes the work and has gained some confidence she can come back into College and do a one-year Rural School training course."

I could have kissed the man's hands. It was an arrangement that should be happy for everyone, including the Dorans who hadn't wanted a College training for Anna in the first place.

"Oh, thank you," I said.

"And now about Miss Wright," he said without looking up. "On whose authority did you go to Miss Wright? I don't recollect she is a tutor of yours?"

He looked at me squarely for a minute.

"I think your action was probably both kind and impulsive," he said slowly. "It was, however, a matter of extreme bad manners."

I said nothing.

"You may go now," he said after a minute. He rose and walked round his desk, opened the door for me.

"Have you ever thought of taking up writing as a career?" he asked. I almost whirled round on him. Did he even know one's dreams?

There was a little sly smile on his lips.

"When I read your essays I am always reminded of the professional journalist. Not so much real knowledge as a flair for words and a fertile imagination. Less attention to Mr. Denton and Mr. Donoghue, estimable though they may be, and more to Mr. Richardson's lectures and your writing will improve beyond recognition."

I faded out the door; but I still loved the dear man.

8

GREEN FIELDS OF YANNANOO

NNA and I felt our return to Yannanoo was something in the nature of a triumphal progress.

This was the moment for which I had dreamed night and day for thirteen long weeks. As for Anna, she was bringing back to her family the thing they wanted, a posting to the little school at Yannanoo. Of the sad day which had brought about this miracle not a word was to be said. Neither Anna nor I foresaw that while they were satisfied with the materialistic result of this term's work they faintly would feel that somehow Anna, a Doran, had not pulled it off in competition with those city folk. What is more I, a solid representative of those same city folk, was still holding my own down there at College.

All this was something I later read in the atmosphere but which for the moment I did not anticipate. My whole body and mind was taken up with the sheer thrill of being here again.

Where would Jake be? What would he say, when he saw me? Would he care that I had come back again, would he ever know that I came back because of him; and that all those lovely sights, winking lamps on a musty station, creaking leathers on a creaking trap, the glorious and never to be forgotten smell of hay ripening in the first of the spring winds were the sights and sounds of a dream upon which the heart fed? Would Jake know that for three months he had lived with me days and nights, the cherished object of all my foolish, childish dreams? And would he have thought of me at all?

We climbed the last rise, and there was Bee at the gate. All was exactly as before. No detail in that picture had altered. Only my own feelings were changed.

Jake shook hands with me. And yes, he was glad to see me. His face wreathed in a grin; the dark, odd eyes held something shy and tender that flickered in their depths a moment and then like a frightened thing was gone. If there was nothing more in it than this, he was *glad* I had come back. He had forgotten, or at least forgiven, my impulsive argumentative tongue. I fed ravenously on

197

that smile and on the tiny glow in the depths of his eyes.

But I was awkward and clumsy. I wanted Time to stand still so that I might savour every second of this minute, but nothing remained still, not even my nervous and frightened tongue.

I talked too much. I rattled on to hide my nervousness and my huge and uncontrollable delight in being here again.

The Dorans were silent and watchful, anxious.

Every little silence seemed a challenge to me. It was as if all of them in the room, all the things that were in it, were waiting for me to go on. With all my will I tried to be silent. But their waiting-ness, their eyes on me, the unasked question hovering continuously in the air, the sense of anti-climax in every pause—these things opened the floodgates of the great reservoir of words that God and my father, in an eternal conspiracy, had endowed me with. When I couldn't remember any more anecdotes I made some up. When I exhausted descriptions of my family and friends I invented new descriptions and philosophies. I talked, my God, how I talked!

The gladness in me gradually died away and I felt ineffably sad.

All the time, from the moment we had drawn into the siding at Yannanoo, I had given rein to a great flow of young, ardent and incoherent love; the sort of unbidden welling of tumultuous and half-understood feeling that only a young person knows and inevitably feels only with one's first love. And I was tired and spent.

There I had to sit on that evening, my true love guarded by the amazonian silence of his family.

The tempo of my talking quietened and died away. They had laughed with me, but the laughter had not come from their hearts.

My sadness was the grief of the frustrated, conscious of the prize he seeks and cannot reach.

Next day I busied myself with Anna, waiting again for the great moment of the day—sundown. With the resilience of youth my spirits emerged again embattled with the belief that I had been mistaken on the previous night and that the Dorans loved me after all.

After the boys came home dinner was delayed for three-quarters of an hour because

Anna was closeted in the dark little study with Jake and Mrs. Doran.

With their customary secretiveness none of the Dorans mentioned this conference. It was never referred to again. Anna emerged smiling and therefore silence sealed the subject of the Teachers' College.

In Anna's new happiness, however, there lay real tragedy for me. It was *her* tongue now that was loosed, and what she felt as gratitude to me, the one who had helped bring about this miracle of release, she expressed in a sudden adulation of me and all my ways.

"Theodora's the most *wonderful* person in College," she said at dinner. "She has them all eating out of her hand . . . from Professor Angus to Paddy Donoghue."

"Paddy Donoghue?" Mrs. Doran suddenly lifted a sharply interested ear.

"Oh pshaw! He's nothing." Anna's eyes sparkled across the table at me. "He's just an also-ran, isn't he, Theodora?"

"Oh, for goodness' sake, Anna . . ." I pleaded. My eyes besought her but she was too inept to read their prayer.

"Is this a friend of Theodora's?" asked

Bessy. I could see a sudden sly interest in her pale blue eyes.

Anna laughed merrily.

"Oh, not Paddy Donoghue. Not really. It's Paul Denton who is Theodora's love. You should see *him*. Tall, handsome, clever. The idol of the College. *Everybody's* mad about him! The girls can't take their eyes off him, but it's Theodora who's got him. It's what's called a *real* affair of the heart!"

My dinner was a wedge in my throat. The slow red mounted over my breast and neck and face.

My voice was harsh and unreal.

"What nonsense. We're friends, just friends."

The Dorans laughed joyously.

"We know all about that."

"Why, Theodora, your face is going red all over!"

Anna smiled slyly.

"Just wait till I tell them about those backstairs and a certain young lady who comes in *hours* after roll-call. And it's little Anna who remembers to brush the twigs off her coat next morning."

How they laughed! Except Helen. She watched me, wary and grim. She hadn't been home when I had come to Yannanoo before. She was like her mother, big, fair, strong and implacable. And she could smell out man-hunters by instinct.

"What does your mother say to that?" she asked thus underlining the hint of un-morality about coming in late at night.

"Look," I said desperately. "Paul Denton's a friend of mine. We talk . . . that's all. . . ."

"Now, now, Theodora!" they all shrieked. "You can't get out of it that way."

"Look," I said again. "A girl doesn't have to have a love affair with every man she knows. I know lots of men. . . ."

"Quite a gallery," Anna interrupted proudly.

"Anna, you're a fool," I said bitterly.

"Don't be angry, darling. I *know* you're faithful to Paul."

"Quite a social success," said Bill suddenly. He was always one sentence behind in conversation. He had Helen's grim look. He had also the aspect of the male suddenly awake to the wicked shallowness of women.

"How *many* scalps have you got round that belt of yours, Theodora?" asked Mrs. Doran with a wide smile on her broad strong face.

I looked round the table. It was the only way I could bring my eyes to Jake. He was

202

eating slowly. His black eyes looked away and the long black-lashed lids drooped over them as he looked at his plate. Shy men like Jake don't compete for the kind of girl the Dorans were making of me.

Jake, Jake, my heart said. Don't believe them. I'm not shallow. I'm not a cheap flirt!

Then Anna told them Paul's history.

"I knew his father," said Bill suddenly with scornful interest. "He was a mining man. Then took up a big place down Katanning way. Why," said Bill. "Why! That chap, old Denton's son, he comes into the Prince of Wales hotel at Royal Show time. A big fellow with yellow hair. Why, he's just a pansy! He's nothing more'n a big blustering know-all."

"No," I said fiercely.

I defended Paul, perhaps unduly labouring his good points and skimming his faults.

Jake was looking at me now. His eyes were focused sharply on my face and in his there was no longer any kindness, or any shyness either.

"A tall chap with bright yellow hair?" Jake remembered and didn't like Paul Denton and I was damned by my defence of him. As I looked at Jake I saw him reject Paul utterly.

And with Paul went me. It was as quick and final as the turning out of a light.

I shook my head because I could not believe that death could come so quickly, and with so little warning.

"He's just a so-and-so walking-stick," said Bill.

"That's what Theodora likes," said Bessy slyly. "A walking-stick. Lots of scalps. Lots of good times."

"Well, good luck to her," said Janet tersely. "Wish I was in her shoes myself. Not a man within coo-ee of Yannanoo."

This scalp-hunting talk was clever. It immediately reduced anyone who showed an interest in Theodora Montgomery to the status of a scalp on a belt. No male would stand for that, let alone a male whose prestige in the eyes of his family was as high as Jake's, or even Bill's.

They were psychologists, these Dorans.

"Don't you take any notice of them," said Mrs. Doran. "You have a good time while you're young. Why, they're all jealous and I'm ashamed of them."

But she nodded and smiled as she spoke and they knew right well she wasn't ashamed of them. They knew she knew what they were all up to.

All except Jake. What would he know of feminine intrigue?

He ate his dinner, his face empty of all expression except, as I saw with a pang, one of extreme tiredness.

"I suppose we'll be hearing of an engagement any minute?" said Bessy. Oh heaven, I thought. They've almost got me at the altar. Before midnight they'll have me in bed with Paul.

Quite suddenly I knew they were capable of even that.

In the end it came from Bessy.

"*What do you do* so very late at night that Anna has to pick the twigs off your coat next morning?"

Anna began to sing our song. . . .

"Down by the river,
Summer nights I lie,
Stones for my pillow,
And for roof the sky."

She laughed across the table at me knowingly, too young and inexperienced herself to know the suggestion behind Bessy's question and her own capping of it with the song.

I turned my head sideways a little and stole a glance at Jake. There was nothing in his face. Nothing at all. He was not there.

If he had ever uttered one word that would have given me the right to explain myself, I could have saved the day. But I didn't know, had never known, if he really cared even a fig for me.

Night after night the teasing went on endlessly.

Once I was alone on the veranda and Jake came round the side path and stepped up on the veranda and stood looking at me uncertainly. His dungarees were stained with the loam of the fields and there was mud on his boots, and some on his face. I half-started up in my chair. But it was no good. Helen stood in the doorway surveying us.

"Jake," she said gently reproving. "That's no way to appear before a lady. Why in town all the young men have clean faces, haven't they, Theodora?"

"I like Jake dirty. Please, Jake, stay dirty for me!"

But it was no good. Helen came on to the veranda and sat down beside me. She smiled with kindly and understanding wisdom at her brother. I knew then it was no good.

I stayed until the end of the week and then went back to "Forty-five."

I said good-bye without feeling. My wounded pride told me that I had no place in this woman-ridden house, and who wants to be judged like a head of cattle anyway? Deep in my heart I gave myself the lie. He had not wanted my love.

Mostly when we look back in life we laugh at ourselves and our own loves. But I don't think a first love is such a laughing matter, after all. It's no odds what sort of a girl she is; when she gives her first love it is something to her that is precious and of purest ray serene. The shades of the prison-house have not quite closed upon her spirit. Her heart is never quite the same again, her love never quite so guileless or sincere.

And so it was with Theodora Montgomery.

9

TWILIGHT

WHEN College re-opened there was no Paul. Word came that he had been gored by a bull while on holiday. He was recovering but would be a week or two late.

"Just like Paul," said Paddy who had been with him. "Walks through the flaming paddock, right under the bull's nose, and waves a billy-can of tea at it. Bull takes one look at Paul and heaves him in the air."

We walked the pine avenue alone, bereft. Paddy had no Paul and I no Anna. And no dreams either.

I planned a vast campaign of work. It seemed now that work was the only thing that mattered and I sat late hours over books.

"What's caused this turning over of a new leaf?" Sam Richardson asked me as I sat with him in his study. Sam looked at me with his quizzical, blue, long-lashed eyes. It seemed to me now that he was a fount of wisdom. I listened to his words humbly and something in them, some opening up of other vistas of knowledge, had their healing effect. Things that Sam said could never scintillate as did the bright facets of Paul's erudition. They did not glitter with brilliance nor excite with exotic ideas, but they were analytical and when he followed an idea to its logical conclusion it was impaled upon the point of truth.

In that interim period between the beginning of term and Paul's return I had the feeling of taking refuge in Sam's wisdom. I went almost nightly to Sam's study, sometimes in a group with other students and sometimes alone.

I was oddly drawn to Sam's company because there was something secure and comforting about him. I didn't mind the long, thoughtful, quizzical looks he gave me. I didn't mind that he probably saw in that analysis of me the skeleton of a dill, because I thought Sam was the kind of person who accepted dills and was gentle with them just as he accepted and was gentle with all other brands of student animal.

All the same, College wasn't the same without Paul.

The first intimation of his return was

Paddy whistling through his fingers to me outside the gym hall after dinner.

"Hey! Do you know who's back? He's down by the gate."

I ran down the driveway, past the pines. Paul was standing waiting, his hands in his pockets.

I was gladder than words to see him again and I reached up and kissed him. At the same moment Paul's arms went round me and we kissed again. We didn't care that half the College was looking on. We were both full of gladness. Paul tucked my arm in his and we started off down the river road.

"Hi!" panted Paddy from the rear. "Wait for me, you two. What the heck do you think you're doing going without me?"

We stood still and waited. We laughed and linked arms and half-walked half-skipped towards the river.

"Down by the river," we sang. "Summer
    nights I lie,
Stones for my pillow, and for roof the sky."

It was spring and the nights were drawing out, the sky was a mystery blue and the water lay serene and darkling.

"Ah, it was gay, night and day,
Fair and stormy weather,
Fiddle and I, wandering by,
Over the hills together."

We sang lustily, killing sorrow with gladness,
strangling sadness with song.

We talked and told lies about the good time
we'd had out of College and we laughed
noisily at Paddy.

At half past eight he stood up.

"I'm going up to the pub," he said.
"Another half an hour to go before closing
time. I've got some money, believe it or not,
and by heck I'm going to spend it."

"Give you half an hour," said Paul. "You
can't get drunk in that time."

"Half an hour it is," said Paddy. The pub
was out of bounds for College students, but
on this night we knew no rules.

Paul and I sat and talked now. For once
Paul had ceased consciously to scintillate. He
was talking of his hopes and ambitions. He
would finish a degree at the University and
then take honours. He had spent his holidays
planning his career and he meant to make it
an academic one. He would go to England
and do a Master's degree; then to America.

The world would be his . . . he was avid for possession.

We didn't notice that Paddy had been gone an hour. Perhaps about half past nine we heard him crashing through the arundinaceous places. Under his arm was a great newspaper bundle of fish and chips, and the breath of hops preceded him.

"Sorry, you blokes. Met a man. Had to have a talk with him. Ver' nice chap. Knows all about the man in the moon. Had a drink with him."

"Paddy, you're just the littlest bit squiffy."

"Inebriated's correct word," he said sententiously. "'S a ver' good feeling. Ver' good night, ver' good beer." He slapped me affectionately on the shoulder. "Ver' good friends too," he said.

"This is his way of celebrating your return," I said to Paul.

We began to eat the fish and chips while Paddy gave a detailed personal history of everybody he met in the pub. When he had finished we washed our hands in the river and rubbed them in the sand.

Paddy picked up my hand and began to stroke it.

"Nice long hands, Theodora," he said.

"Soft as a paddy paw. Never did a hard day's work in their life."

"Quite right," I said. I wasn't going to buy into an argument with Paddy. He turned my hand over and kissed it in the palm, the soft warm touch of his lips suddenly gave me a sense of unreality and desolation.

"You know what," said Paddy. "You got a terrible name . . . Theodora. What a mouthful! Theodora . . . My-adora. That's it. My-adora. By golly, My-adora . . . I-Adora!"

Paul snorted.

"Throw him off. He's drunk."

I didn't reply. The kiss in the palm of my hand had wakened untold longings in me, but because I was both innocent and ignorant I didn't know what was the matter with me. I had thought that Paul's return would put everything right with College, but quite suddenly it didn't seem to do so at all. It was not Paul that I had wanted but something else. Something to do with a frustrated dream, something to do with wanting to love and be loved . . . but by neither Paul nor Paddy.

"Throw him off," said Paul again.

"I like him," I said simply, without moving. A little bit drunk, Paddy was a little bit childish and a little bit dear.

"So this is how it is," he said coldly.

"Don't be an ass," I said.

"We wouldn't be one too many, would we?" asked Paul with immense scorn in his voice. "You two are not thinking of reducing this meeting to a petting party?"

Paddy lifted his head up.

"You know what?" he said. "That's a darn good idea. You go 'way and leave My-adora to me. G'wan Paul. You're one too many."

"If my return is to be celebrated with this sort of party . . ." he said coldly.

"G'wan," said Paddy. "Scram! You're not wanted!"

"Are you coming, Theodora?"

"Sit down, Paul, and don't be an ass," I said. "I don't want to go back. I want to stay here. I don't mind Paddy. He's only the littlest bit drunk. He's putting most of it on."

"G'wan," said Paddy. "Not drunk. Stone cold sober. Never more sober in my life. I want to talk to Theodora."

"Certainly," said Paul. He took a step or two away, hesitated, obviously waiting to be called back.

"I know you're there," said Paddy. "Hop it!"

He strode off through the reeds, making enough noise for a brigade.

Paddy chuckled.

"Poor old Paul," he said sagely. "Never been told to go away in his life. Just can't believe it, can he?"

Paddy put his head back on my shoulder.

"What did you do it for, Paddy?"

"Dunno. Wanted to hear what Paul sounded like when someone told him to hop it. Anyhow what 'ud *you* stop for?"

"I don't know either. It's just the river . . . and the night . . . and the mood. I just don't want to go back."

I put one arm round Paddy and leaned my cheek against his curly head. Somehow it suddenly seemed so sweet. This moment now by the river . . . the reeds so stiff and still, the river still and moonlit with silver. The stars, the incredible bright stars! They were the same stars that shone now on the ring-barked trees of Allanson's, the winding track climbing up the valley to the homestead where the lights winked and wherein there sat a small dark man immersed in papers.

A tear wedged itself from under my lashes,

rolled heavily down my cheek and fell on Paddy's face.

He sat up suddenly.

"Girrl darrlin'!" he said, very Irish in his concern.

"Nothing, Paddy," I said. But I let the tears, only a few of them, but very big fat ones, roll down my face.

"Blow your nose, darrlin'," he said. I did so loudly.

"It's not that bastard Paul, is it? My God, Theodora, you're not in love with Paul, are you?"

"No, it's not Paul."

"Someone else?"

"Yes, someone else."

"I'll punch his so-and-so head in."

"No need, Paddy," I said. "After all he didn't ask me to fall in love with him. Anyhow he didn't want me."

"Don't believe it," said Paddy flatly. "What went wrong?"

"He had a family."

Paddy groaned. We sat and brooded on the river.

"My God," he said. "I want to have a good cry myself."

"Whatever for?"

"Dunno. Just the time, and the place, and the food."

"I'll tell you what it is, Paddy. We're just two stinking Irishmen. We can't control our emotions. We sit here and weep and in the years to come we'll look back and think that these are the years the locusts have eaten. We'll burn with regret and longing for this time that will never come again. We'll long for this time when we sat by the river and fell passionately in love with it, and with the moon, and the reeds, and the old dark College behind us. And it will all be gone for ever and we will never be able to find it again. But now, while we've got it, all we do is sit and weep."

"Beautifully said, darrlin'," Paddy said. He rubbed his cheek against me and his hands caressed mine. "You know what, Myadora? When I'm in bed at night I can hear your voice, and see your face, and I wonder what will become of you. I wonder who will be kind to you, and understand you. Who will find the pilgrim soul in you . . ."

"Oh, Paddy," I said. We had our arms around one another now. "That was the speech of the evening! But you've been reading W. B. Yeats."

217

"I have that," he said rubbing his coarse curly hair against my cheek.

"How many loved your moments of glad
  grace,
And loved your beauty with love false or true;
But one man loved the pilgrim soul in you,
And loved the sorrows of your changing face."

"Paddy darling," I said. "No one else in the world but you could quote a poem like that at a woman and get away with it."

He reached up and drew his fingers down my face.

"My Adora," he said. "Nobody can get away with anything with you. Darrlin', I wouldn't marry you if you were the only woman on earth."

"Why not?"

"It would be like marrying a volcano."

"Is all that in my 'changing' face?"

"That's just what's in it, darrlin'. 'Tis a fine face, but turbulent and troubled. And who is there to understand it and know why it sometimes fills itself with all the sorrows of the world! What's going on behind those stormy eyes, darrlin'?"

"Old Dr. Riley used to say my father had a

bird singing in his breast. I wonder what the song would have been if he could ever have uttered it. He was a stinking Irishman too. You know, Paddy, Paul doesn't understand the Irish. He thinks we're amusing and pleasant company for trifling, but he doesn't understand the tearful part about us."

"Do we understand it ourselves?" he asked. Then suddenly he sat up. "For God's sake, Theodora . . . what in hell are we doing? Blubbering like a couple of beastly adolescents. Get off your seat and come home."

We stood up and shook ourselves then we linked arms and walked down the river road.

"Snap out of it," said Paddy.

We began to sing "Fiddle and I." After a while I stopped singing and listened to Paddy. He had a light baritone with a tender quality in it that was thick with the Irish brogue.

"You've a lovely voice, Paddy," I said. "You know what? You'll either become a great teacher and sing and laugh your way through your children's hearts, or you'll just become a hopeless and rather low-down drunk. That's what always happens to Irishmen. They hit the heights or they hit the depths."

"That's the solemn truth, my girl," said Paddy. He was suddenly reminded of his role of slight inebriation and staggered a little. I put my arm around his neck and my head on his shoulder. He was very dear and I was miserable. He held me gently and comforted me with his mouth on my hair. There were footsteps coming across the turf around the corner.

"What in the name of fortune is this?"

It was Sam looking at us. "Aren't you by any chance weeping on the shoulder of the wrong man?"

"Oh, mind your own business," I said rudely. "And I'm not weeping."

"Certainly," said Paddy. "Respectable people mind their own business at this hour of night." He pretended to be still a little drunk and he began to shape up as if for a fight.

"Cut that out," said Sam evenly.

"Don't take any notice of him," I implored Sam. "He's a boxer. Don't egg him on to show off."

"Absolutely right, My-adora," said Paddy. "Don't worry, darrlin'. Shan't lay a finger on him. If I did I'd plaster him against the pines."

"Oh shut up, Paddy," I said miserably.

"Do you want to go inside?" Sam asked looking at me.

"Yes, I think so," I said. "We've had about enough of it. Good night, Paddy darling. Be good."

"Well I'm damned," said Paddy to our retreating backs. "Off she goes with a musty so-and-so of a gum-nut like Sam."

In the dim light of the hall he looked down at me sardonically.

"Now *this* situation would take some explaining away," he said. "Staff letting in the students after roll-call."

"More evidence of Sam's night-life," I said feebly. "I hope they won't sack you."

"I've taken the sack myself. I've been appointed Lecturer in Education at the University. I won't be here next term."

"Oh, Sam. I'm sorry. There'll be nobody left next term but me. Paul's going full time to the University. Anna's gone and Paddy's only taking a rural course. He finishes this year too. I won't even be seeing you any more."

His hands were in his pockets again and he looked at me with his head slightly on one side.

"Yes, you will. I'm coming to tea next Sunday night with Mrs. Montgomery. If I measure up I might be asked again. Bill Jennings has arranged it all. . . ."

I laughed. "He would," I said.

"Is it all right for me to come?" Sam asked.

"God help you, Sam," I said weakly. "All the Montgomerys are mad."

"I've noticed that," he said. He patted me gently on the head. "Not a bad kind of madness, though, especially as seen in Theodora."

"Sam," I said coming back. "Did you mean just a little bit of that?"

"Just a little bit, Theodora. Only the most infinitesimal bit."

He was smiling at me.

"I'm not entirely a worthless baggage?"

"Not entirely."

"I'm not a complete dill in Education?"

"Not completely."

"Then you give me a decent mark next tutorial or I'll blackmail you."

"You're doing that now," he said.

I had a feeling his eyes were a little too serious so I retreated up the staircase post haste. I leaned over the banister and looked down at him.

"Sam," I said softly. "It's not polite to look at a lady going up the stairs . . . too much leg!"

"Too much cheek," said Sam. But he grinned at me.

All the same it was none of these that I thought when my head hit the pillow. But I shed no more tears.

10

IN THE FOREST

OUR fevered interest in work threw Paul and me together more than ever, and my sentimental mood of the night by the river was forgotten and never repeated. I was sentimental again and on other occasions but never in such a manner and in such company.

We inundated Sam and other tutors with enthusiastic diatribes on our discoveries but these efforts were mostly treated with the scepticism they merited.

Sam had come once or twice to "Forty-five" with Bill Jennings and he settled down to being what we Montgomerys called—one of the onlookers. He didn't take sides in our partisan arguments; he didn't become more than friendly with one or other of us; he didn't seem an *essential* part of our way of living as Bill Jennings and Evan Burns were, but the Montgomerys liked him and welcomed him—and didn't notice when he wasn't there. Heaven only knows why he came.

Towards the end of term Paul and I did a senseless, futile thing. We became engaged.

I wonder, even to this day, how it ever came about. I think it was as both Paddy and I had said on that night down by the river . . . a matter of the time, the place, the mood.

The year had worn away. Much of it was taken up with hard work. We sat long hours in the library. It seemed to me as if there never would be time to consume all the books I hungered for.

Underneath this avid thirst for the printed word was beginning to grow a feeling of insecurity and unrest. The end of the year brought an atmosphere pervaded with sadness. We knew that when this year came to an end no other would be quite like it. Next year I would be alone in the College.

The three of us thought we were about to lose something precious when we lost one another and that time would never send others to fill the place. Each of us knew we were getting a little too old to be silly, and the silliness had been half the joy of our companionship.

Paddy went first. On his last day in College we were out of our various beds by five in the morning, walked on empty stomachs the four miles to Cottesloe beach and had a swim in the Indian Ocean. We came back to College with wet heads and tired legs, our voices shrill with the last of our adolescent laughter, but a sorry, and for the moment inadmissable, pain in our hearts.

That night Paul and Paddy made a night of it. History has it that Paddy and his baggage were put aboard the train by the most able of his carousing friends. I did not hear of Paul for two days. He emerged white-faced, black rims to his eyes and a flow of curses for his head that would have done a bullocky justice.

After that we didn't talk about Paddy. We felt as if one of our limbs had been amputated.

I was twenty and he was twenty-two.

We read A. E. Housman continuously and went about quoting him.

"Lie down, lie down, young yeoman;
The sun moves always west;
The road one treads to labour
Will lead one home to rest,
And that will be the best."

This was Paul's favourite as we went down the drive between the pines. We inevitably ended with . . .

"When I was one and twenty
I heard a wise man say,
'Give crowns and pounds and guineas
But not your heart away . . .'"

We became horribly morbid and I put down the fact of our engagement largely to the influence of Housman.

On the eve of the closing of College for the vacation we walked through the moonlight to the place we had been for our last swim with Paddy. The beach sands were cold beneath the touch of our fingers and the ocean was still and indifferent.

"Farewell to barn and stack and tree,"
shouted Paul to the sea.

"Farewell to Severn shore.
Terence, look your last at me,
For I come home no more."

He flung his arm around me and I clung to him quite pathetically.

"I wish you strength to bring you pride,"

this time he was shouting at me.

"And a love to keep you clean,
And I wish you luck, come Lammastide,
At racing on the green."

"Look Paul," I said miserably. "You don't have to say 'goodbye' to me. After all the University is only six miles away, and I'll be going up there for Education and Psychology."

"We don't ever have to say good-bye," said Paul with sudden and brave conviction. "Do you realise, Theodora, that we've become necessary to each other? We're part of the same life. All day I've been trying to deny it but now I know it is the solemn truth. It is fate."

All of which, of course, was tommy-rot, but we believed it, believing in the terror of our impending loneliness.

We refused to be lonely. So we became engaged.

We did not announce our engagement immediately. Paul delayed his departure from town three days while we thrashed the matter out.

He had his ambitions for the next four years. First his degree, then a higher degree, preferably in Britain. I had my bond with the Education Department. It was a three-year contract for service. Moreover, I had an obligation to my mother and family. I wanted to be an assistant bread-winner for a few years, at any rate.

It seemed to us a highly satisfactory state of affairs that both of us considered matrimony was impossible for at least four years. Deep in the very secret fastnesses of our hearts we did not really want to be married, though we didn't know it. We were unwilling that either should contract another friendship, and so we bound ourselves to each other.

We kissed one another, but not lavishly. That should have told us something. Perhaps it did and neither of us listened.

The Montgomerys gave the engagement a mixed reception. My sisters were fond of Paul and proud of the glamour of good looks and high-brow learning that he carried about with him. They were quite pleased to see me "carry off" the prize, as it were. But some fundamental insight into the matter told them the truth. They did not put it into words but I knew they were doubtful about its success.

Mother, worldly wise, had no doubts whatever. She was determinedly opposed to a long engagement. She tried to warn me of its pitfalls and dangers, but she was too shy and too Victorian to tell the real truth, even if she realised it herself. And I was too ignorant to understand what she was trying to tell me.

We lived in the moment and every moment held some new pleasure. Immediately after Christmas, Paul came back to Perth and we strutted about together, self-consciously. I was inordinately proud to be seen with him. I was surprised and pleased at his pride in the Montgomerys. He boasted of our achievement and wore his relationship with us like a halo rewarded only to the chosen.

And our achievements were not inconsiderable considering our long and deadly struggle against poverty. This was the first vacation since I was fifteen when I had not worked to help balance the budget. Mary, her nose relentlessly in her text books, was gathering distinctions for herself in the Law School at the University. Vicky, always dainty and well-turned-out, was still the idol of old Mrs. Baston's heart. She wore with her, as she went about, the aura of being the familiar of people of wealth and consequence. Denney had blossomed into rare beauty. She was tall, like a willow, and her great violet eyes beneath their arched brows and the square Montgomery forehead, looked with an intriguing insolence upon an awakening world. Gerry, still young but handsome in a striking way, was making a niche in a circle of friends as the family comedienne. She had a ready and spicy wit, a flow of anecdote and a guileless way of "putting her foot in it" that drew roars of delighted laughter from any circle of listeners, young or old.

If sometimes in the fastnesses of the dark and secretive night I had a twinge of doubt, it was because, unsummoned, there rose before the inner eye a memory picture of a horseman pounding the turf up the rise of the hill to the stable-yards. I did not face the question then, but I have not the slightest doubt that for all my surface happiness and my pride and affection for Paul, if a certain farmer from way up in the Grasslands had but lifted his little finger, Theodora would have left her bed, her place with her family, her all, and flown immediate and obedient to his side.

She took what happiness lay about her now because she knew with utter and irrevocable finality that little finger would never lift.

In the second week in January Paul and I went south to meet his family.

I had not known the depths and heights and secret loveliness of Australian forest country. I was awed and struck to the heart by the great vast beauty of these sentinel trees thickly studding a green and verdant land. Everywhere hung the mystic scent of the eucalypt.

My first glimpse of Ellington, the Dentons' property, told me more than a series of books about Paul's family history.

Here was no home carved out of a reluctant land; no wealth won by relentless toil, responsible judgment and indefatigable fidelity to a heritage, such as I had seen at Yannanoo.

Here was a place upon which money had been despoiled. It flowered with the wealth of the land because the wealth of the gold mines had been expended upon it. To me, reared in the genteel shabbiness of a Rectory and later in struggling gentility of a second-rate boarding-house, here was the home of Midas.

Great stone buildings squatted on the rich earth like a small, active and comfortable township. The house itself, one-storied, large, solid with great stone blocks, was comfortable with all the secret airs of being set upon foundations of solid capital.

Paul's sister, Irene, came down the path to meet us. I had been feeling uneasy about meeting her. Somewhere in me a memory of the Doran sisters had rung a bell and at the end of the year my spirit had been too weary to contemplate rising again to that endless duel of wit and teasing that seemed necessary between a man's sisters and any woman who set foot in the sacred precincts of his home.

A glow of relief and pleasure flowed through my bloodstream when Irene came forward, both hands out-stretched, her eyes soft and full of welcome, her voice gentle and kind.

Her eyes were brown and warm, her small features even and her mouth red and smiling. She kissed me on the cheek and then turned to Paul. I could see there was a bond of affection between them and the girl Paul had chosen was good enough for Irene.

Mrs. Denton stood in matriarchal silence and greeted us in a manner that was exactly correct, neither more nor less. Her dark brown eyes gleamed in her narrow lids and her face was secretive and selfish.

I had enough sense to know that no woman freely gives away her only son, even an erring and prodigal son, without first discovering for herself what manner of woman it is who seeks to take him away. I was determined to be as nice to her as possible without attempting to ingratiate myself.

In one way I was puzzled. Why had Paul left all this? Why had he washed his hands of his heritage?

I had an answer in part, but I never thought it answer enough. Paul was a student, a lover of books. He was not a farmer. But surely there was enough money in this place for him to have had his book learning? The real story, I believed lay in some secret animosity between mother and son. Some intention on her part to impose her will and some resistance on Paul's part that drove him away from the place he loved best.

Yet for me it seemed as if there was some mystery in that denial of forest. In this remote corner of Australia was man's last attainment—a grand and glorious forest.

The extraordinary thing was that Paul

thought so too. We spent our days walking down its cathedral lanes, stirring the small things out of the earth and laughing at one another through veils of sarsaparilla and trailing bush creepers that wound through the undergrowth and hung in festoons from the branches of the saplings.

Mrs. Denton's matriarchal coldness remained Roman and formidable. She spoke often of the property's inability to maintain another family on it. It was gradually borne in on me that she stood a bulwark of defence, not of her son, but of her acres.

This did not disturb me. I was too busy enjoying myself. Moreover, I was aware of two fundamental truths, one in Paul and the other in myself. Paul himself was a match for his mother. If he wanted me he would take me and all her hostility would be put at nought. For myself my experience with the Dorans in the Grasslands had killed my terror of a man's relatives.

What hardness had the land bred in the hearts of the women that they saw in a young woman's eyes, not the capacity to love, but only avariciousness for what the land could offer in terms of pounds, shillings and pence?

I was sorry about Mrs. Denton's attitude,

but in my secret heart I was contemptuous of it. The wealth of Ellington impressed me but did not tempt me. I had never known real comfort and so never hankered after it. I was at the age when love in a cottage would have been heaven indeed if the loved and the loving were of the same mind.

After a fortnight I went back to Perth. Paul was to come up within the next two weeks and neither of us realised that in the joy of being together we had mistaken high spirits for true love; companionship for an affinity of natures; and the fact that we recognised a sensitivity to beauty in each of us led us to believe that we had a divine insight into the very working of our hearts. We couldn't have been more blind.

Professor Angus who had been in Albany was travelling on the express to Perth. I blithely told him my news. He received the knowledge of my engagement to Paul with a chilly bleakness. He was formal in his felicitations but he turned away as if something had happened bitterly to disappoint him.

I told myself that his disappointment lay in the fear that he might lose Paul, the best student he had had in years. Perhaps he visualised an impending marriage. I shied away from the possibility that he thought we were not really well matched.

We sat and talked in the lounge car for some time and I found myself telling him, not of the place in the deep forest, but of the farm in the Grasslands. When I spoke of a horseman it was not of Paul's gay braggadocio on fidgety horses but of a short dark man welded in the saddle of a thoroughbred.

I think now that Professor Angus saw through the wool I had pulled over my own eyes.

I said good night and wove my way down the narrow corridors to my sleeping berth. If I was a little chilled in spirit I put it down to the sadness of farewell, even though the farewell was for so short a time.

Part Three

THE WORLD AT LAST

1

DENNEY GOES FIRST

I ARRIVED at "Forty-five" about mid-morning to find Sam Richardson in the arm-chair reading the paper.

"How did you get here?" I asked.

"I came up with Bill Jennings."

Sam surveyed me, with both hands in his pockets.

"Been down at Paul's place?" he said.

"M—m," I said. "Lovely place. Lovely holiday. Beautiful rich fertile land. All they have to do down there is throw in the seed, then jump clear."

I was pushing my hair into place and looking at him in the mirror of the big sideboard. He didn't think I was being clever and he knew I didn't care about the Denton money. He just looked at me as if wondering mildly why I was trying to be clever.

"What are you looking at?" I asked turning round.

"I wasn't looking, I was speculating. So

241

you two have really done it?" He gave me the kind of look that said neither Paul nor I had much taste.

"Now you be good about it, Sam," I said. "You're not going to lose Paul as a student. He's going to finish his degree first."

"And what about you?" he asked. "Is Professor Angus going to let you come up to the University for Education?"

"It's a fact, Sam!" I said. "You'll have me sitting at your feet all next year."

There were disturbing sounds at the front door.

Two pairs of feet were advancing down the passage and then Denney stood framed in the doorway. Over her shoulder was a man's big, strong, amiable face.

"Where's Mother?" said Denney. "Oh hallo, Sam. You know John, don't you? This is my sister Theodora . . . John Hastings."

So Denney had carried out her threat and brought her man home!

He came into the room now and shook hands with Sam. He was a big man, rather old in his ways, his face good-looking in the hard kind of way that men who have spent years in the bush are hard. He shook hands with me and grinned amiably. Then he looked at Denney. Even I, with all the inherent hostility of sisters-at-loggerheads, caught my breath at the loveliness of the picture she made. She swayed slightly on her hips like a young sapling. She had almost perfect features, though some might have said the Montgomery nose and forehead were too consciously arrogant. Her eyes under arched brows were the indescribable violet blue of fiction. She looked so fresh and young and unconquerable.

"Mother's at work, of course," I said scathingly. "And why aren't you at College?"

"I've left," she said tersely. She turned to her man.

"Come on, John," she said. "You'll have to help me pack."

"Pack what?" I was startled.

"Mind your own business," said Denney airily but without any animosity.

"Denney," I called. "Don't take John in your room. Mother doesn't allow *that*."

She didn't bother to answer and we could hear the sound of drawers being dragged out and cases pulled from under the bed.

"What on earth . . .?"

Sam leaned back in his chair and smiled.

"Perhaps she's going for a holiday too.

Perhaps her young man is taking *her* down to meet his people."

"Don't be silly, Sam. Denney's only seventeen and a half. She can't get engaged at that age. That's different. Besides nobody knows this John."

"Well, you're wrong about nobody knowing him," said Sam sagely. "Denney's been bringing John home for nearly a fortnight. Mrs. Monty's quite attached to him."

"How do you know?" I asked bewildered. "Have you been roosting here for a fortnight too?"

"Pretty nearly," said Sam. "Mrs. Monty and I like each other."

"Sam," I said drawing in the corners of my mouth. "Who've you been coming here to see?"

"Quite frankly, nobody in particular." He smiled at me. "After all you were away, Theodora. . . ."

"All the more reason to look amongst the other four."

"No, Theodora," he said. "I'm just a good listener . . . and all of you are amazingly good talkers."

"The gift of the gab," I said. "It's a tyranny on all our friends and neighbours. Anyhow if you want a young lady, Sam, there's always dozens of them drooling in with one or other of us. Maybe you'll meet the right person, someone really grand at the Montgomerys'."

He shook his head gravely.

"I'm not the marrying kind, but it's obliging of you to think of it."

"Don't be sarcastic, Sam," I said. I looked him over. What a good match he'd be for someone! Someone nice and academic with a quiet dignified manner and a string of degrees after her name. Oh well, Mary was the one to produce something in that line. Mary's friends were mostly academic.

There was the sound of dumping cases in the hall and Denney came down the passage into the kitchen. John came after her. We heard sounds of the kettle being filled and put on the stove.

"Sounds like tea," I said getting up wearily. "I might as well set the table and turn it into lunch. I wonder if Bill will have enough sense to bring something eatable and in sufficient quantities. Seems Denney and this John are going to lunch with us too."

"Maybe I'd better go for something," Sam said getting to his feet.

"Well, milk's always useful," I said. "Do

you think you'd mind going down the street with a billy-can?"

"Why should I?" said Sam looking surprised. I couldn't tell him that I had odd moments when I remembered that he was my tutor in Education and that I could hardly ask so august a person to wander about West Perth with a billy-can of milk in his hand.

In a sense I was a little nervous of him but at the same time wholly his servant as far as our student-tutor relationship was concerned. Maybe I talked a bit freely to him sometimes, but that was only my manner, and at the same time I certainly didn't like packing him off down the street on domestic errands. While he was away, Bill came back with Mary and one of Mary's friends. Between the three of them they carried a large bag of tomatoes, some crispy French bread and a jar of cream.

We were in the throes of putting the lunch on the table when Mother came into the room.

Her face was broad with a smile of welcome for everyone. I felt instinctively she had let a heavy cloak of weariness drop from her shoulders before she crossed the threshold.

This was one of the occasions when I thought the young people really came to the house to see Mother and it was only fortuitous that they became friendly squires for the girls.

Without even a glance at her hair she sat down in her place. It came on her quite suddenly that Denney should have been at Business College.

"Why are you home, Denney?" she asked suddenly lifting her head. Her eyes took in John and the blue dress which was Denney's best. She looked from Denney to me, puzzled. "Are those your suit-cases in the hall, Theodora? They look very like Denney's."

"They're mine," said Denney. "John and I are going to get married."

We dropped our knives and forks and stared.

"Married?" said Mother.

"Yes," said Denney. "John has a new job in Bunbury. We want to catch the five o'clock train."

She looked at Mother with her shameless blue eyes. Not a muscle twitched on her face. She simply sat, her eyes defiant, her chin up, her spirit obviously indomitable.

Mother's eyes slowly shifted to John's face.

"What have you got to say about that, John?"

He grinned.

"Just what Denney says," he said. "We want to get married. We came back for Denney's things and to get your permission."

"You won't get that," she said sharply. "How old are you?"

"Twenty-eight."

"Eleven years older than Denney and . . ."

"Ten and a half," interrupted Denney.

"You know, of course, that Denney's under age. You could be prosecuted for enticement."

"Yes, but you wouldn't do it," said John softly. "We want to get married. Nothing wrong with that. Why should we wait? After all, my mother was married at seventeen and I'll bet you weren't much older, Mrs. Monty."

"Don't argue, John," said Denney. "You never get anywhere with Mother by arguing. Just tell her we're going by the five o'clock train and if she gives us her permission we can get married. If she doesn't we'll be living in sin."

Knowing Denney so well, even this took my breath away.

Mother looked at John sharply.

"You're liable for a charge of abduction if you do that," she said.

"But you wouldn't do it, Mrs. Monty," said John.

"Wouldn't I?" flashed back Mother.

Denney held out her hand to John.

"Give her the paper," she said. John fumbled in his pocket and brought out a form. Denney handed it to Mother.

"You sign on the dotted line," she said. "We can get married when we get to Bunbury."

"What makes you think, Denney, I'd let you do a thing like that?" she said slowly.

"Because of Mary," said Denney evenly and without lifting her eyes from her food.

"Mary? What's it got to do with Mary?"

"Mary and Vicky," she said. She looked up now and her eyes were hard and defiant. "Vicky knows all the *right* people. It wouldn't do to shock them. And Mary wouldn't like the disgrace of a sister living in sin. She's got her career to think about. Her career as a lawyer . . . you know, the thing with a wig on that goes to court."

A red stain mounted Mary's neck but she went on eating, silent.

"Oh, let her go, Mama," I said. "After all, it's one less mouth to feed."

Denney's blue eyes fixed me in contemptuous regard.

She's very lovely, I thought with a pang in
my heart. What a waste!

The colour was mounting in Mother's face.
Her chin came forward in a familiar bulldog
manner. It was the chin that had won a living
for us out of destitution.

"I'll do nothing of the sort," she said.
"Denney's too young to know her own mind.
She'll meet half a dozen young men and be in
love with them before she marries."

She fixed John with an angry eye.

"I don't think you have placed yourself in a
very admirable position. You have come into
this house, where there is no man to protect
us, you have abused our hospitality. That,
however, is nothing compared with the want
of principle in inducing a girl as young as
Denney to go away with you."

"John's got nothing to do with it . . ." began
Denney. "I said I was going with him. . . ."

"Hold your tongue," said Mother tartly.
"If I could, I'd thrash you."

John was unperturbed.

"Those arguments which you have used
against me ought to carry weight," he said
quietly. "But they don't. They're just

arguments for face-saving in a silly world. There's nothing wrong with marriage. It's the natural thing for any young man and woman to undertake. There's nothing wrong with me. I'm a trained surveyor. I've got a good job and can keep and take care of Denney. And biologically seventeen and a half is not too young for marriage."

I was beginning to admire him. I liked his calm assurance and I agreed with the logic of his facts. I was interested in his lack of any attempt to ingratiate himself with us, or to excuse his action. He was quite indifferent to us. We were used to people finding us either a wonderful family or wholly impossible.

I decided that Denney had more in her than her sisters were ever likely to see. To have made a significant impression on this self-contained young man took some doing.

Some of us had finished our lunch and Bill now stirred.

"I think I'll be getting along, Mrs. Monty," he said. "I've got a kind of feeling that this should be a family conference. Sorry to have barged in on it."

"Don't apologise, Bill," I said. "I don't know any family skeleton hunt you haven't been in on."

"Coming, Sam?" he said.

The two men stood up. Sam looked shy though not embarrassed. We had, as a family, a habit of staging these sort of scenes without causing anyone discomfort.

Mary was the only one who longed for a little privacy. Denney was hitting Mary on her most vulnerable spot now.

"Take Mary with you," she said belligerently to Sam and Bill. "It would be beneath her legal dignity to have a finger in this sort of low pie."

Mary's face was white. Her head leaned forward a little, a gesture habitual of her disapproval and of a certain grim determination.

She pushed back her chair.

Sam was standing at the top of the table with his hands in his pockets. He was looking at us all with grave humour. Then he moved round the table to shake hands with Mother.

"I expect he thinks we're all hell-bent," I said sourly to my plate.

"On the contrary I think you're all six for heaven," he said, smiling at Mother. It was the nicest thing he could have said to her, for it made her one with her five daughters and the tears smartened behind her eyes.

When they went out there was a momentary silence in the room.

"Well, what about it, Mrs. Monty?" John asked leaning forward across the table.

"No," Mother said violently. "Never." Then the tears packed up behind her eyes. "If only I had a man to help me . . . to guide me, and give me advice.

"Denney has always been the outlaw," Mother said bitterly, as if Denney was not there.

"Come on, John," Denney said. "We'll get a taxi."

Mother sat immovable. We could hear them going into the hall and carrying the suitcases outside.

They had gone.

Mother sat still. She stared at the piece of paper in front of her. "Sign on the dotted line," Denney had said. Now she had gone away with John to "live in sin." We were both afraid she wasn't bluffing.

"Why don't you let her go, Mama?" I said. "Send the piece of paper after her. She'll be off your hands then. John will have to look after her."

Mother looked up at me.

"You only say that because you've never

253

got on with Denney," she said with sudden insight. "You'd like her out of the house. You'd be at peace then. Her happiness and welfare mean nothing to you."

"Why should she mean so much to you, Mama?" I said. "She's always been the outlaw of the family. Look at the way she persecutes Mary. Is that fair? As for me . . . she's never been anything but a torment to me. But all that aside, how can you stop her now? Why not legalise the thing? If she makes this bed for herself she must lie down in it. And like it."

Mother sat on in silence. The hard stone quality of her expression gradually drained from her face and in its place there came such a look of sorrow that I felt it like a stroke on my heart.

Her child had gone from her. A rib had been torn from her body. I saw her sitting there at the table, long after all had gone, her face heavy and brooding in its sorrow. I saw that it was not so much Denney that mattered as that of Mother's life, something she had nursed and that had been part of her body had gone.

I got up and went to the telephone. I rang the genteel Girls' College where Vicky fulfilled the functions of genteel secretary.

"You'd better come home, Vicky," I said. "Mother's in a 'state-of-mind.' You'll know best what to do for her."

"What is it? What is it?" Vicky was saying, anxious and haughty.

"Denney. She's cleared out. Gone off with John Hastings."

Vicky's voice began to gurgle and choke with indignation and an immediate sense of outraged dignity. Such information to be coming out of the telephone and pouring into the *nice* little office of the Girls' College!

I hung up the receiver and went back to Mother.

She got up wearily and went to the arm-chair. She rested her elbow on the thick padded arm and bowing her head on her hand she wept. To me it was a terrible sight. I had seen Mother weep before, but had never seen her thus bowed and broken. Always before it was as if there remained some fundamental strength that would ultimately reassert itself. But now it seemed as if all the sorrows of her life were multiplied in one burden which bowed her spirit down to the very ground.

Gerry came flying in from Business College. One sight of Mother in the arm-chair and Gerry was in hysterics.

"What is it, Mama darling? What is it, Mama darling?" She flung her case aside and was on her knees, her arms wound round Mother.

Gerry and Vicky were the slaves Mother needed.

Presently Vicky came in and the pantomime proceeded.

"Awful *creature*," Vicky said of Denney. She was imperious in her wrath. "Never mind her, Mama. We'll look after you. We're still here with you. Never think of Denney again, darling," and then in a low involuntary aside, "*Wretched wretch* that she is."

And Mother began to rally. The distress of her two daughters called forth the maternal instinct again and she came to their rescue. It was her turn to comfort and pacify now.

"It will be all right," she said. "I will fill in the form and send it to them. There will be no disgrace. I shall arrange everything properly. Theodora, get me the ink and writing-pad. I'll send the form and a letter to Canon Hitchings. He was a friend of your father's and he will marry them in the Church. He will do that for me . . . for us all, dears."

256

She was patting Gerry's tousled head and she looked at Vicky pityingly.

"Poor Vicky!" she said. "Brought all this way home from work! Never mind, dear, go and have a good rest now. You'll get over it presently. Why look at Theodora and me!"

"I will never get over it," said Vicky tragically. "After the years we've spent building up our good name and holding our own! The *shame*, the *disgrace* of it." Tears of self-pity filled her eyes.

"Theodora," Mother said in a cajoling tone. "Bring Vicky a cup of tea, dear. She shouldn't be upset like this. It's not good for her to rush up from work in this manner. Poor Vicky!"

There was a footstep in the passage and as I went outside I bumped into Bill.

"So it's *poor* Vicky now is it?" he said in a whisper.

"Inevitably!" I said bitterly. "Here, you come and get a cup of tea for her. You know what I'll do with it if I keep on feeling the way I do about Vicky at this moment."

"For the love of Mike, give it to me," said Bill anxiously.

I was in too bad a mood to give Vicky credit for the really tender heart she had. She expressed it in warm and loving caresses to Mother, something which I could never do, and I think that is why Mother loved her—and Gerry—above us all.

"Tea for all!" shouted Bill. "Give me that flaming bit of paper, Mrs. Monty. I'll take it to Bunbury myself. I've just talked the paper into sending me down there on a job. If I look slick I'll catch the five o'clock train myself."

"Oh, Bill . . ." said Mother.

Even I felt my heart suddenly warm towards him.

"Cup of tea, Theodora?"

"Thanks, Bill . . . Say Bill . . .!"

But I couldn't say it. Instead my eyes filled with tears.

"Take it as said, darling," Bill said. He swallowed his tea, took possession of the fateful form and was gone down the street with a flurry of flying boots.

"That is a good boy," said Mother. And she looked at me reproachfully.

2

THE END OF YOUTH

IN February I went back to College. It is probably heresy to say so, but the absence of Paul and Paddy was of more benefit than loss. I did more work.

The first few months passed simply enough, but towards the end of the first term storm clouds were mounting on the horizon of my private world and once again my emotional life had to impinge again on the intellectual, and always to the detriment of the latter.

I went to Sam Richardson's lectures in Education at the University. He sent for me one day. He sat looking at my essay with a thoughtful frown on his brow.

"What *is* wrong with them, Sam?"

"Too many words, Theodora. To me, a word is an instrument to help convey a thought. The thought should be traced to its logical conclusion by a procession of words, and to that end the words should be simple

259

and direct in their application. To you, it seems as if they are toys, perhaps jewels to be played with for their own sake."

He leaned forward and with a pencil indicated a passage that had been marked on one of the pages.

"You see you have said that three times. First you say it fairly simply and then you suddenly spread yourself and make a literary repetition of it."

I re-read the passage for myself.

"But I've put the information there," I said puzzled. "What I have said is correct. On your own admission that is what the papers are marked on. Don't I get credit for *knowing* and drawing the right conclusion regardless of how I express it?"

Sam shook his head.

"It becomes a matter of comparison," he said. "I mark twenty essays on this subject and I naturally give higher marks to the one who writes the matter down simply and clearly. I think it's a better paper even though both students have the same knowledge.

"Look," he said. "Take this that you have written here, and spent half a page on it . . . I would put it this way. . . ."

And in a few sentences Sam had reduced

260

my fine efforts at writing to a simple state-ment in almost single syllable words.

"I couldn't do it, Sam," I said. "I know you're supposed to be right . . . you're the lec-turer and I'm only the student, but even if the barest pass mark depended on it I couldn't write that way. Maybe I wouldn't have infor-mation in sufficient quantity . . . maybe I've just got to *feel* what I write. You're too cold, Sam."

"Perhaps you are right, for your way of do-ing things, Theodora," he said at length. "But you won't hold it against me that I give higher marks for a simple exposition, will you?"

I smiled.

"We agree to differ?"

He relaxed and came to the door with me.

"How's Paul?" he said smiling down at me.

"Lousy," I said.

"I guess you're not a rich man, Sam, so maybe you'll smile at this one too. . . . He's lousy because he's worried about money."

"Money?" said Sam. "I thought they had it in plenty."

"They have," I said. "But they don't like giving it to Paul. It's bringing out the worst in him."

261

"I hope the repercussions aren't too serious on Theodora?"

"Fair to middling only," I said.

I went away feeling kindly disposed to Sam. I thought we'd both done a bit of educating one another on the subject of how to write tutorials.

But Paul? My feelings there were another matter.

The University had opened for Paul wider horizons than even he had dreamed of. He was restless. Professor Angus saw this and mourned. He couldn't keep his hands on the destiny of this bright young man and within the first few weeks Paul had switched from Education to Philosophy and Literature and was trying to induce his family to pay his way through the University so that he could free himself from the Education Department and the Teachers' College. His family resisted. There were no teaching fees charged in the University and the College was prepared to house and board Paul provided he remained a member of the profession and entered into bond to give so many years of service in return for his training. It was against this that Paul rebelled. The University opened up new vistas, and distant horizons beckoned.

I think Paul wanted to have his cake, and eat it. He wanted me for his girl friend but his future was bound up with his own desires. Our joint future was something so remote and distant that it wasn't even worth discussing.

I knew I would never pin this lesser genius to the confines of our own State. I could not hold him to our companionship and to a destiny here in this remote place on the Australian continent. It was not the University that took him away from me, it was the things that he learned there that whetted his appetite. I knew that inevitably Paul would go into the blue.

In the meantime we had to go through the sad and sorry process of discovering this, and of being frank with one another about it.

The engagement had intangibly altered our relation with one another. We were asked out together. If we did not go together the matter was wondered and commented upon. This hurt either or both of us, but we still resisted the social insistence on tying us together on all occasions. There was constant friction between us and our parents on the subject of social obligations.

"Paul *must* go with you," Mother said on

one occasion in connection with an invitation to afternoon tea at the Bastons'. "Mrs. Baston will consider it a discourtesy if he doesn't go."

"But Mama, he's not interested in them. And they're not interested in him. They've only asked him because they think it's incorrect to ask me without him. Can't I ever go and have tea again with Susan and Margaret without taking Paul?"

Mother said stubbornly, "There are certain social conventions to which you must conform, otherwise people's feelings are hurt."

But I went without Paul all the same. I knew the Bastons would bore him stiff and I knew they wouldn't like his highbrow liberalism in politics.

"Paul didn't come with you?" said Mrs. Baston with raised eyebrows. "When Richard was courting me he couldn't bear to let me out of his sight for a moment. Well, well, times have changed of course."

"When Lionel was engaged to Anne," Susan said. "He wouldn't *allow* her to go out without him. He considered it his *privilege* to squire her round."

And quite irrationally I was furious with Paul for not being the doting, chivalrous

264

squire. I would entirely omit from my chagrined thoughts the fact that I hadn't even told Paul that Mrs. Baston had included him in the invitation.

But irrespective of these things, we argued now about abstract things, and often with animosity and an edge to our tongues. It didn't seem to me now that the things Paul said were so very splendid after all. The clever, colourful things he used to say he no longer seemed to utter. I thought his intellectual postures were irrational and that they were opportunist.

And as for me . . . I remained a trampler.

We were two egoists and the result of our engagement was friction.

Beneath it all, however, there was a strong bond of affection. We would hate one another, realise with utter and irrevocable finality that we had had enough of each other. Then within a day or two we were together again, perplexed and amazed that we had not seen the light which was for ever shining in one another's eyes.

Nevertheless, time was acting as a corrosive agent in our relations.

Paul was worried about his family's resistance to his pleas for financial help. He was over-working. He smoked too many cigarettes and he kept bad hours.

It was at this stage that both Paul and Paddy intervened to open my eyes to what an engagement really meant and what marriage should really involve.

I had been in the country for a long week-end and had come back to Perth to attend a ball with Paul. Mary and Evan Burns were also going and we had arranged to go together.

I didn't see or hear from Paul during the day, which was odd, since I had been away since the previous Friday, but I did not think overmuch about it. I was too busy going to the hairdresser and putting the finishing touches to my ball dress.

Mary and I bathed, powdered and scented ourselves and sat down in all our glory to wait for Paul. Evan had been in the house for dinner.

A whole hour passed with Mary and Evan forcing the conversation and Mother trying not to let me see she was worrying.

"He's had a break-down in that silly car," I said to Mary. "You and Evan go on. We'll look for you as soon as we get there."

When they had gone I sat staring into the fire.

"Do you think by any chance that Paul has forgotten?" Mother said gently.

"Quite possibly," I said.

Another half-hour passed. We were sitting by the fire in the dining-room and I could see myself in the big mirror of the sideboard. I knew I looked good. Though I'd made it myself I knew my dress was a success. Yet I was sitting there waiting for a man who I was almost certain would not come.

When I heard the sound of his car rounding the corner and coming to a stop outside "Forty-five," I still knew it wasn't Paul. I knew he wouldn't come, and I knew I would never forgive him . . . whatever the reason.

It wasn't Paul in a dinner jacket at the front door, either. It was Paddy Donoghue.

"Paddy dear!" I said. "I'm in full evening dress so I shan't attempt to hide my humiliation from you. You've come from Paul, haven't you? I suppose he deputised you to take his girl friend out?"

Paddy put his arm round me:

"Don't crush me, Paddy."

He pulled me hard against his chest.

"Don't be bitter, My-adora. It doesn't suit

you. I've come from Paul. But he doesn't know it's in dinner jacket or that I'm going to take you out."

"I don't know that *I* know it either."

"You're coming out with me, Theodora. Get your cloak. I've got Paul's car."

"Where's Paul?" I said.

"He's in bed. Sick."

"And there's no such thing as a telephone service?"

Paddy's arm tightened round me till it hurt. His face was close to mine and his eyes were commanding.

"Get your cloak, Theodora."

I went into the dining-room and picked up my cloak.

"It's not Paul, Mama," I said. "He's sick. I'm going to see him now with Paddy Donoghue."

I was attempting face-saving and I guess she knew it.

I got into Paul's car and Paddy lit a cigarette and then taking it out of his mouth put it between my lips.

"I came up from Denmark to go to this wedding," he said. "I got here about midday and Paul and I went on the binge. Paul's under the weather."

268

"Don't lie, Paddy," I said. "You're sober now whatever you were at five o'clock. Paul could have maintained the same discipline."

"But he didn't, Theodora," said Paddy. "That's the point."

"But why, Paddy? Why? He knew we were going out to-night."

"I don't really know why. I only know that he did get stinko and that until three-quarters of an hour ago he'd forgotten about the ball. He's dead miserable for some reason . . . and he sank it in pots this afternoon."

We sat in silence for a moment and then Paddy put his arm around me again. He pulled me over against him in that hard compelling way in which he had held me when he came into the house.

"Why is he miserable, My-adora?"

"I don't know."

"Why are you miserable?"

I was silent.

"Listen, darrlin'," said Paddy. "I'm going to show you to-night what's wrong with you . . . only I'm warning you now while I'm sober. You're coming with me, Theodora, and I'm going to show you what you're made of under those dark eyes and that trembling mouth of yours."

"Where are we going?"

"We're going to a wedding. And we're going to have fun. It's a real Mick's wedding . . . Irish as Paddy's pigs . . . and champagne all the way."

He was speaking very quietly.

"It ought to be fun, but your voice doesn't sound it. What's the matter, Paddy?"

He rubbed his curly head on my cheek.

"I'm taking you out to learn about life," he said. "When we come home and I'm drunk you'll remember that it was all premeditated, won't you, darrlin' . . . and you'll understand why."

I felt curious about the region of the midriff. Was Paddy going to get me drunk too? What was going to happen to me?

"Start up the old bus," I said. "Let's go on to this wedding there's so much talk about."

We drove across the town. In a small side street, littered with parked motor vehicles of all sizes and vintages, we pulled up by a medium-sized house where celebrations were obviously afoot.

We went inside and nobody took any notice of us. We pushed our way through a crowded passage to a large rear room where the bridal couple sat on a raised dais on the far side. The room was full of people sitting in semi-circle rows facing the bridal pair and listening to a pair of pipers making their peculiar squeaking noise.

Paddy put his fingers on his lips and we sat down on two low seats. A man put his hand around my shoulder and there was a shallow glass offered to me. Obviously the champagne of which Paddy spoke. A minute later there was a glass in his hand too.

The audience was rapt. In every hand was a glass of pale yellow bubbly. Outside the people in the passage were talking noisily but inside there was no sound but that of the pipers.

The piping came to an end and the applause was generous but restrained. People began to push in from the passage now and I could see several jostling for standing room around the walls.

I raised an eyebrow to Paddy.

"More piping?" I asked.

He winked.

"It's only the beginning," he said. "The fun'll start soon. That's why the crowd's coming into the room."

Suddenly he was recognised by someone and he had to get up and join a group of men who began slapping his shoulders happily. I was left alone on my low seat with a glass of bubbly in my hand. I looked around as I sipped the champagne. It looked like a middling working-class home. Comfortable in its own way. I couldn't place the people about me. Then I caught sight of the hands. Men and women alike . . . their hands were calloused with hard work and there was black sand engrained in the palms of the men's hands.

"They're growers," I thought. "That's what it is. Out here on the outskirts of the suburbs are the big market gardens . . . the Irish and the Yugoslavs."

Corks were popping everywhere and it seemed as if everyone had to fill their glasses in readiness for something. Then the pipers began again. This time it was something gay and sprightly. Feet tapped on the floor and glasses were constantly being raised in silent toasting. More and more people rushed into the room and it began to be noisy. I thought the champagne was probably working its oracle. The music grew faster and the feet thumped. Someone near the door began to beat a kettledrum.

I looked around for Paddy and could only

see the top of his head in the middle of a group of Fenian giants.

Was I going to sit here all night and listen to this weird noise . . . and, of course, occasionally sip champagne?

Presently a girl dressed in kilts stood up and she danced on the dais near the bridal couple. I presumed it was the Irish jig. It gave inordinate pleasure to the audience which clapped to keep in time. At specified intervals they shouted "hoi" in unison.

Presently the pipers came to an end and they threaded their way through the room and disappeared. Only the kettledrum kept up a low persistent tattoo. The noise was now terrific. Everyone was talking and laughing. Faces were flushed and voices were loud, though heavy with the Irish brogue. A big man stood up near the dais and began to shout at another man across the room. The other man shouted back. Everyone laughed at them. Then the man by the dais began to dance a jig on the spot. The laughter was full of delight.

All the time the kettledrum kept up the low tattoo.

I looked round for Paddy. I saw him standing by the wall with men on either side of him. He had a wineglass in his hand and though the men all seemed to be talking to him at once, I could see he wasn't listening. He was looking at me, his head bent forward a little, so that he looked at me under lowered brows. His eyes seemed very strange.

He looked at me for a minute or two without making any signal and then he left the talkers, without giving them a word, and pushed his way through the room to me.

He looked down at me and his eyes were still strange.

"Well, My-adora?"

"Are they all mad, Paddy?" I asked.

"No, only Irish," he said.

"But Paddy," I said. "There's nothing funny about them! Their humour's so crude! It's not even smutty. And yet everyone laughs."

"Why don't you laugh, darrlin'?" he said.

"Paddy, I *can't*. It's not *funny*. And that kettledrum! It's getting me down!"

"That's what it's meant to do," he said. Then he began to laugh. He laughed in the wheezy hilarious way we used to laugh when we all three walked together down by the river. It was infectious and went on and on.

"That's awful funny, Theodora," he said

at last. "Only you don't know anything yet."

He slipped down on the low chair beside me and tipped some of the champagne out of his glass into mine. He had his mouth close to my ear.

"The drum is part of the gypsy music," he said. "It goes on like that for a long time. Then the fiddlers begin. That's when it should begin to get you down, darrlin'. People who are addicted to gypsy music are more slaves to it than people addicted to drugs. The drum's only the prelude."

"But nobody's listening to it."

"Yes, they are." he said. "Underneath all that talk and noise they're aware of the drum. It's like nigger tom-toms in the depths of the African jungle. But with gypsy music the fiddles make it more subtle. Just you wait, My-adora."

A bottle of champagne came over his shoulder and our glasses werc filled.

"How much of this stuff can one drink without getting drunk?" I asked.

"You're all right so long as you stop inside," Paddy said. "I'll take care of you when we go out into the air."

I raised my brows at Paddy.

"Go on, darrlin'," he said. "You're Irish too! Let it go . . ."

What *was* the effect of champagne on one anyway? I felt myself slipping. The tiniest relaxing of my muscles and I would go over. Over and down.

I put out my hand and clutched Paddy. I clung tight to sanity for a moment.

"I'd be loud and vulgar, like those people."

He shook his head.

"Not vulgar, My-adora. Just Irish."

His eyes were hypnotising me.

Was that what was strange in them? Was this really Paddy or some foreign secret Paddy of whom I knew nothing?

"Let it go," he said staring into my eyes.

I started to laugh.

So I'm Irish too . . . what the hell anyway!

The laughter began to choke in my throat and tears came into my eyes.

The big man by the dais turned round and looked at me. He held out his hand.

"Come here, angel," he said.

The big man found me a chair. He brushed the hair back from one of my temples.

"A slightly dishevelled angel," he said and everyone began to laugh. I laughed too and someone put more champagne in my glass.

276

Then the drummer came and sat down on a stool just below the bridal pair.

I stared at his drum fascinated. The noise no longer worried me. It was quite low, yet gradually I knew it was becoming more and more insistent. Round my midriff I felt awkward again, and slightly queasy. I looked up and found the drummer's eyes on me. He was a young man, swarthy of face with black Latin eyes.

"Are you a gypsy?" I asked. The question sounded silly and my voice didn't seem my voice.

He shook his head.

"Hungarian," he said. "But I learned it from the gypsies." Seemingly from nowhere a man and woman came and sat down beside him. They put their fiddles under their chins and began to play.

At first I couldn't understand it. Only the Hungarian's eyes and the rhythm of the drum held me. Somewhere inside me there was impending excitement.

I looked round for Paddy and he was sitting on a small chintz-covered box, his head bent forward and a little sideways. He was unaware of anything but the music. I saw then that there were quite a lot of people sitting like that. They sat still as if they had been hypnotised. Their eyes were strange.

This winding of the music in and out of the fabric of one's whole make-up, went on agelessly. Sometimes it was resplendent and exciting; sometimes soothing and conciliatory. But all the time was a persistent crying note in the violins. One note with one cry. And remotely buried in it all was the rhythm of the drum.

I lost contact with the earth and breathed only in the realm of the senses.

In all this time Paddy did not speak again. He sat, leaning forward, his elbows on his knees. Occasionally he smoked and occasionally sipped the champagne. It seemed to me as if he were under some profound spell.

Now and again he looked at me, but his eyes were alien.

3

WE CALLED IT A DAY

WE drove in Paul's car back across the southern skyline towards the river. When we had crossed the railway line Paddy turned west and then south again until we came to the familiar river road that led past the College. Paddy drove to the edge of the beach.

I hadn't any idea what the time was. As Paddy had promised, I'd been all right with the champagne until I had come out into the night air. Then Paddy had taken charge. Now he had brought me down to the arundinaceous places, scene of our past innocence. I knew that the only real difference between then and now was that I had since heard gypsy music.

We sat down on the cold grass, our backs to the reeds. I felt the cool night air laving my brow, but it could not clear my head. It was champagne in some part that muzzed me up but mostly it was the throbbing of a drum keeping time with my heart-beat, and the one perpetual cry dominating the melody of the violins that I could not get out of my system.

Paddy lit a cigarette and we smoked it together. When we finished it, he buried the butt in the sand.

With his hand nearest me he took hold of my shoulder. Then slowly he pushed back my cloak until it fell off my shoulders. He leaned over me and his arms were round me tight and hard.

I felt him straining me against him so that my breast hurt against the hardness of his chest. His mouth was on mine, domineering and accepting no denial.

The notes of the violins, the throb of the drum in that magic music surged through me in a passionate knowledge of all that it and Paddy meant.

I threw my arms around him, and yielded my body against his.

Then his body relaxed. His strength, compelling me against him, ebbed away and he leaned over me, heavy with his own weight.

The kiss that had begun as a command had become a caress. It was as primitive as the drum of the gypsy music.

"No, Paddy!" I cried. "No! No!"

I tried to throw him off but his weight was too great.

I twisted my mouth away from him.

I felt his muscles tautening. Gradually he drew himself away from me. He lifted his head and stared at me. The moonlight made his face pale and it was the face of a stranger. It seemed so cold and star-washed. Paddy shook his head like a dog after a swim. He sat up but we didn't speak for a long time.

Then he took my hand, turned it over and kissed the palm as he had done on that night, in this same place, almost a year ago.

"I'm very drunk, My-adora," he said.

I pulled his head against my breast and held him tight for a moment.

"Not drunk, Paddy," I said. "We both knew what we were doing, and why, when we set out to-night."

"In the end was my beginning."

Paddy sat up and pulled my cloak around my shoulders. He turned my face so that the moonlight would shine on it.

"This is the place for Housman, not Eliot," he said. "Listen darling. . . .

"On your midnight pallet lying,
Listen, and undo the door:
Lads that waste the light in sighing
In the dark should sigh no more;
Night should ease a lover's sorrow;
Therefore, since I go to-morrow,
Pity me before."

I shook his hands away.

"I was brought up in a Rectory," I said.
"I'm inhibited to the point of safety."

"Yet you put your arms around me, darr-lin'. I did not dream it."

"Only for a moment, Paddy darling. Only for a moment."

I must have said it as sadly as I felt, for suddenly Paddy picked up one hand again and squeezed it tight.

"Did you like the music, Theodora?"

"Yes. And I understood it. And I know why you took me. And why you brought me here."

He was silent for a minute.

"You now know the sort of person *I* am," he said slowly.

"The sort of persons we both are."

He gave a short laugh.

"No! Paddy. No!" he mimicked me.

"It's the Rectory background," I said. "I'll have to take my love softly muted between the blankets of matrimony."

"Oh God," Paddy said furiously.

"Don't be too disappointed, it wasn't a complete failure as an experiment. I know now why Paul and I are miserable. That is what you meant to teach me, wasn't it?"

"Not exactly," he said quietly. "I meant to teach you what you are yourself, My-adora. Underneath several generations of training in civilised behaviour you are what that gypsy music is. So am I. It's in both our eyes. It's in a good many Celtic people. But in Paul? Never! Paul moves in the realms of Bach and Brahms. You're the kind of person that ought to throw her cap over the windmill, Theodora."

"I know," I answered dully. "But I can't because there's another streak in me. One that is cowardly and falls back on pleas of inhibited training and on senses of duty to family and so on."

"Pure cowardice," said Paddy. Then after a while he patted my hand.

"Have I made you unhappy, Theodora?"

His voice was the voice of the old Paddy. The stranger, the passionate, exotic stranger had disappeared. Paddy, my old friend Paddy, would take me home.

The next day Paul had recovered from his sickness and came down to College to see me. He had a thunderous scowl on his face.

"Where'd you and Paddy go last night?" he asked sulkily.

"You ought to know," I said. "Paddy came up from the bush for a wedding. So to the wedding he went."

"He didn't tell me he was going to take you."

"You shouldn't have sent him up as your messenger boy. You might have guessed I'd be in evening dress. I had been waiting to keep another engagement. Paddy could hardly be so unchivalrous as to leave me stranded."

Paul looked at me suspiciously. I longed to punish him by telling him the truth that Paddy had come with every intention of taking me out and completing my education. But I didn't tell Paul. Mainly for the sake of the friendship between him and Paddy. The engagement was no go, and we both knew it. Paul knew it, otherwise he would not have forgotten me the night before and then taken refuge in drunkenness. I had known it for a long time but since last night I had known it with absolute finality. I knew that when Paul and I were together we moved on a plane so far removed from the physical world that we were only aping the habits and customs of loving couples.

Paddy had taught me the physical aspect of love. It had been Paul's job and it had never entered his head. I thought of his own allegorical tale of the garden. Paul's feet would never trample in the little things of the earth because they would never trample in the mud.

Well, I was glad I'd had my mud bath last night.

"I suppose you know Paddy's got some blonde down there in Denmark he's going to marry. He wanted me to help him buy a diamond ring yesterday."

I started to laugh.

"Paul darling," I said. "You're jealous. You don't really care very much for me at all. But you resent the possibility of my having enjoyed myself with Paddy last night. It's not love that prompts your annoyance. It's wounded vanity. And you did bring it on yourself, you know."

Paul looked coldly aloof.

"I was merely giving you that as a piece of useful information in case Paddy overlooked it."

"As a matter of fact he did," I said gravely. "But it doesn't matter except that I didn't have the opportunity to wish him luck."

I looked at his face, heavy with anger, and wondered where the fine fellow I'd seen that first day in College had gone. Had he changed or was I seeing him without the rose-coloured spectacles? He seemed so different in every way. His attitude to all things was reactionary and autocratic.

I wondered furtively in what way he too had found a change in me. In what and how many ways had I disappointed him.

I said no more about the engagement then, but we both knew what was in the mind of the other. I was intensely relieved that I didn't have to be afraid of hurting Paul, that I didn't have to care about his vanity. Yesterday he had intended to be cruel to me in the most humiliating way possible for a man to be cruel to a girl, but Paddy had taken the weapon out of his hands and turned it on himself. To-day it was Paul who was licking his wounds. To-morrow or the next we would finally sever our engagement.

As I walked back through the park to College I thought about this. I thought about the business of just loving for no other reason than the hedonistic pleasure there was in it. I realised I had never known it with Paul. The only times I had ever felt that slow honey-flow of warm delight, that the gypsy music had told me was earthly love, had been on those occasions in the fastnesses of the night when I had had a sudden unbidden recollection of a small dark man sitting beside the lamp-lit table, buried in his newspaper. Even then, in my ignorance, I had mistaken that feeling for one of regret and sorrow while I had secretly admitted that I knew what I would do if Jake would but crook his little finger.

But he never did.

Instead it was Sam.

I sat in the small chair opposite his table in his study. He was looking at me with that slow deliberate thinking look that made me feel he was taking my mind to bits, and probably finding it wanting. His thick lashes

287

sometimes lowered over his eyes as he looked down at my essay before him.

"Too many words?" I asked.

"I'm afraid so."

I wasn't in the mood for it and the disappointment and sorrow at my own ineptitude must have burgeoned forth in my face. I longed for the woman's prerogative to weep.

"That sort of essay is not Education," he said, not looking at me but speaking rather through the window as if he was reflecting and not holding a conversation. After a long pause he added . . . "But it is fine writing."

"What do you know about fine writing, Sam?" I asked bitterly. "You told me that words were only the instruments for thoughts. Their value is purely utilitarian."

He turned round and leaned against the window-frame.

"For me, Theodora. For me. But then I have not been blessed with the seeing eye and the hearing heart when it comes to the things that grow and walk and crawl on the earth."

"What do you mean, Sam? You are not trying to tell me that I have got something that you haven't got?"

"Yes, I am," he said. I could see his face now the shadow was off it. The lines were suddenly a little drawn and sad. He looked older than he really was.

"Somewhere inside you, Theodora, there is something worth while . . . and I think rather beautiful. But it is something I have never touched or seen or known for myself. Yet I know it exists. And I know it exists in you. Some awareness of beauty, the light that never was on sea or land, the light the poets know."

I closed my eyes tight. Oh Heaven, I must not weep. Two nights ago Paddy was teaching me this thing was my memory of the primordial mire, to-day Sam is trying to tell me it is something fine. Father, come back from the grave and help me! What is that bird that was singing in your breast? It sings in mine.

Sam was speaking again and I opened my eyes.

"Why don't you go away and write it all down?"

"Write what down?"

"What you were thinking then when you closed your eyes."

I felt my eyes hard and bright.

"You would never know, Sam, what I was thinking then. You would never know what prayer a girl can sometimes send out into an empty heaven."

"No," he said thoughtfully. "Not unless you wrote it down.

"Begin at the beginning, the day you were born was the beginning of your life, you know. I can't think of a more important date."

"Nobody would ever want to read it."

"That doesn't matter," he said gently. "To become a writer one must discipline one's craft and workmanship. You haven't got that discipline yet, Theodora. You can only learn by doing."

"Sam," I said piteously. "Those words of mine! Those many, many words. Won't people hate them?"

"No," he said. "If anyone reads them they won't hate them. I know that because I don't hate them. I don't always understand them and I often think them out of place. But I often think them very beautiful."

Suddenly he leaned across his table and put out his hand. I put mine in his.

He came round his table, still holding my hand, and drew me to my feet.

"Go and start, Theodora," he said gently.

That night Paul and I broke off our engagement.

"It's no go," I said.

"No," he said morosely. "It's no bloody go."

We were silent.

"Paul," I said. "Have you ever listened to gypsy music!"

He turned his eyes on me and there was faint annoyance in them.

"Has Paddy been trying to interest you in those Hungarian gypsies out at Wanneroo?" he said.

"They were at the wedding we went to."

"The Irish are addicted to gypsy music," he said harshly. "It's fit only for peasants and southern Europeans."

"Well, it's hardly the same as Bach and Brahms," I said meekly.

"I should think not," he said loftily. "I tried to wean Paddy of it a year ago. He's a dilettante, which is a pity, as he has the makings of being a first-class musician."

We were silent again for a while.

"About this engagement . . ." he said at last. "What will you do with yourself now?"

"I'm going to write a book."

His whole frame tensed with interest.

291

"Bravo," he said. "Then I will have served some purpose in life."

We parted without hurt or animosity.

At first the weeks seemed empty and forlorn and sometimes the tears of loneliness would come unbidden when I was alone at night. When however the weeks stretched into the months and the hurt had healed we were able to meet again without pain to either of us. It seemed then that I met again the old Paul I had first known in College. The old affection came back, never quite to fade and be forgotten.

On the night we had broken off our engagement I went home to "Forty-five" to tell Mother instead of back to College.

I found a letter there from Paddy.

"Darling," he wrote.

"My blonde has lit out with the leading footballer in the district. There's a nice brunette, likely to be suitable, behind the counter in the local store. That is if you don't want me. I thought I'd better do the right thing and offer myself. In the event of a refusal can you forgive and forget?

Always my love, Paddy."

I wrote back.

"Paddy dear,
"It's sad about the blonde but being a brunette myself you won't be surprised to hear
me say blondes are twopence a pound anyway. I'd definitely plump for the lass behind
the counter if I were you. She's on the spot
and probably educable. About the other matter . . . I'm sorry to say I can't forget. Who
wants to anyway?
Always my love to you, dear,
Theodora."

Of my broken engagement with Paul my
sisters said not a word. Denney sent me a box
of powder with the prayer that I take the
shine off my nose forthwith. Gerry gave me
two packets of expensive cigarettes from her
secret hoard. Vicky made me several cups of
tea and put her hot-water bottle in my bed.
Mary lent me her beautifully indexed notes
on the modern poets. Since Mary cherished
her books above all things on earth this touched
me to the heart.
But not a word did they say.
Only Mother delivered herself of her pride
in her daughters.

"There's one thing about you girls, you stick together," she said. "When all's well with the world you're all at sixes and sevens. But let one of you be in trouble! You're kindness itself to one another. At heart you're all good girls. You stick together."

Something inside me recoiled and shrivelled.

Mama, must you put it into words!

4

A KNOCKING AT THE DOOR

I SAT behind a large green baize table and stared at sixty small faces.

It seemed as if the College days were long, long ago. In reality I had only been in my first teaching post three weeks. I had come to a town where everyone called me Miss Montgomery and nobody knew that my name was Theodora. I was living in a second-rate boarding-house run by somebody else and because my eyes had begun to bother me and I sometimes wore horn-rimmed glasses the other "guests" in the house spoke of me as the "school-teacher."

I had come to Stirling, a railway centre for the outlying wheat-growing districts, on a day when the temperature hit 108 degrees. I had lived in a bath of perspiration ever since.

The air at night hung about us like a wet cloud and the drumming of the engines of the flour-mill, all the night long, forbade sleep.

Residents of Stirling told me that they did

not hear the mill. They told me they only knew there was a mill in the town when it stopped because then the silence was frightening. It and the heat and the mosquitoes, breeding in the foetid river-bed, were the enemies of my sleep.

I probably would have accepted it all, including the sixty sweating children in a single wood and canvas room, if only somebody had called me Theodora.

I really understood what homesickness had meant to Anna Doran now.

But the "Miss Montgomery" and the "school-teacher" made a foreigner of me, even to myself.

I had spent my vacation beginning on The Book.

It seemed to me, as I looked back, that Sam had said such a simple and obvious thing—"go and write it all down"—that I couldn't understand why I had not thought of it myself. I think the answer lay in a very real timidity. I think I needed someone, and someone of authority, to tell me I could write. To have decided myself to begin writing about my own people, my own impressions of the things and beings that moved about in my immediate world, would have seemed an egotism both unthinkable and inexcusable. But at the very moment when I had closed my eyes and thought of that awful yet beautiful song that strangled the life in my father's breast, Sam had said "go and write it all down." It didn't matter that the song might never be heard, it only mattered to give it life. Sam had said so, and if these had been words coming from the mouth of God I could not have believed more firmly.

At first the words came pouring from me, torrential in their release. Then in a moment of curiosity I re-read them, and I knew them for rubbish. For every thousand words that survived the paper-basket I wrote five thousand. For every moment of radiant hope and inspired creative impulse I had ten of boredom and despair.

At the end of two months' vacation spent almost entirely in writing I had salvaged one useful thing. That was the knowledge that for me it was a long hard way. As Sam had previously said, as Professor Angus had hinted, my writing had never been disciplined, my words had only mattered in their millions and not in their meaning.

By day I was "Miss Montgomery", the

bewildered new "school-teacher", more than intimidated by the enormous class of sixty children. By night I was a writer of words. Even at this stage I was too frightened to admit that I was a writer of books.

Thus at the end of the third week I sat gazing at my children and wondering how I had strength to go on and face the day.

"'S terribul hot day, isn't it, miss?"

I looked into the sallow face and black eyes of the young bare-footed savage who stood beside me. This boy called Caesar. The roll recorded him as Angus MacLaren, but I never could find anything Scottish about him. To all appearances he was plain Spaniard.

Everyone in the school had told me about Caesar. Nobody wanted to teach him. He wrecked nearly every class he was in.

"It's a terribly hot day, Caesar," I said.

His black eyes glittered. He didn't know whether I was making fun of him or not. Everyone in the town and in the playground called him Caesar. But not the school-teachers, they stuck rigidly to roll decorum.

He tried another tack.

"There'll be a bush-fire to-day," he said, his head down and the black eyes never leav-

298

ing my face. I did show some interest now.

"A bush-fire? How do you know?"

" 'Soney half past nine, an' it's over a hundred or-ready."

I looked up at the children.

"Is Caesar right?" I asked. They answered me by the dozen. It appeared that it was over a hundred because they all knew temperatures by various personal reactions of their own and temperatures only got to such a height at so early an hour of the morning when bush-fires were imminent.

Caesar was gazing at me spell-bound. He wasn't interested in telling me about the bush-fires; he was interested in discovering that I hadn't tried to insult him when I called him by his nick-name, and that I hadn't done it to ingratiate myself with him, for peace' sake.

Suddenly the mill whistle blew one piercing shriek.

"Bush-fire!" They all shouted.

Caesar uncrossed his legs, stood up and grinned.

"Told you so, miss," he said.

The class sat quite still in graven silence. Then Caesar hitched his pants and leaned on the table again.

"'S in the north," he said dogmatically.

"How do you know?" I said.

The whole class began to tell me. I banged on the table with a ruler, but it was Caesar who silenced his mates.

"Shut up, you," he said turning to them. His underlip hung out like a bruiser's and his black eyes menaced. He picked up a paper-weight and made play as if to throw it.

Like angels the children composed their faces into listening attitudes.

"I'm torkin'," said Caesar.

He turned to me again and relaxed on to the table.

"One whistle fer north, two fer south, three fer west, four fer east. Then if it stops blowing only the fire brigade goes out. It ain't blown any mor' so there's no need fer anyone else to go."

"What if it does blow some more?"

Caesar shook his head pityingly.

"Two short whistles, spare men wanted. Three whistles all fit men in the town have to go. Everybody over eighteen goes and the town has to shut up. Four whistles the whole town, 'cept children, has to go and children has to stop indoors."

"What about your mother?" I asked eyeing

300

Caesar suspiciously. I knew there were three children under school age in Caesar's family and I wasn't sure that the story wasn't a little tall.

"Not *her*," he said. "*She* wouldn't be any good. It means womin who kin go and cart kerosene tins of tea and help with accidents."

The class began to interject with information. They had given Caesar a good hearing and recognised the point at which he was satisfied in having had his say.

The heat was intolerable and the sky was becoming overcast. A curious grey green colour enveloped everything. Not a wisp of air moved.

I looked wearily at the sallow-faced boy by my table.

"Don't you think you'd better go back to your seat, Angus?" I said.

He looked at me belligerently.

Why had I changed from Caesar to Angus?

There was no reason and after a second's peering into my face he too saw that. He saw that I had other things on my mind. He was deliberating as to whether life was more endurable sitting in his rightful seat or standing, very nearly a rebel, by my table when the mill whistle blew two short staccato whistles.

301

"Streuth!" said Caesar. He hitched his pants with enthusiasm this time. "Thought she was a beaut! Look at the air. Full of cinders!"

He wiped his hand across his brow and looked at it. His hand was dirty and so was his brow. I wiped my handkerchief across mine and looked at it. It might have been wiped across the kitchen stove. We were slowly being enveloped in a pall of smoke.

Then three whistles blew.

The children said "Ooo!" in unison and their eyes goggled. I looked to Caesar for assistance.

"Give out some pad paper," I said. "We'll draw all the people going to the fire."

The children began to hunt lethargically in their bags for coloured pencils and rubbers.

The streets were moving with people now. Some were running, some were on bicycles. All faces were turned to the north.

In spite of the heat and the awful ennui something inside me responded to that urge to excitement called forth by that mill whistle.

"If four whistles go, I'm going," I said aloud, impulsively.

The children gazed at me startled. All except Caesar. He went on giving out large sheets of paper but he spoke to me much as a teacher would to a difficult child.

"You can't go, miss," he said patiently. "You gotta stop here an' look after the kids. Yore the same as my mum who's got little kids at home. You ain't allowed ter go."

"And we ain't allowed to go either!" a child said morosely.

"We ain't even allowed to go home after school unless the all-clear has gone."

I looked at Caesar imploringly.

"Is that so?"

"That's so, miss," he said.

The mill whistle blew four times!

My heart sank.

I could see the head teacher coming across the gravel playground separating my pavilion from the main building of the school. Caesar chose the moment to finish his paper distribution and strike an attitude leaning against my table. The head teacher came into the room. He looked at Caesar.

"Get back to your seat. If I catch you standing like that again, I'll cane you!"

"Don't stand any nonsense from that boy, Miss Montgomery."

"He's not any trouble," I said.

The head teacher looked at me with dark suspicion. Was I such a raw recruit that I didn't even understand what standards of discipline were required in a school of this nature? A school that recruited most of its children from the poorer scrub farms and the railway workers? He came over to me and spoke in a lower tone.

"You must keep a firm hand on these children on a day like this," he said. "Do you know the office temperature reads 106 degrees already and it's only ten o'clock!"

"It must be higher out here in this room," I said feebly.

"It probably is," he said. "If you need any help, send for me. By the way, I suppose you know we can't disperse the children until the extent of the bush-fire is known and the all-clear given?"

"The children told me," I said.

"You'll probably have to relax your ordinary programme," he said. "But keep them busy, if you can."

He looked at the class.

"Angus MacLaren, out here, sir!"

Caesar sidled out of his seat, hitched his pants and dragged his bare feet out to the front of the class. His black eyes gleamed with hate in his sallow face. Under the thin shirt and pants I could see the muscles rippling like music down his body.

Caesar, an eleven-year-old boy, stood facing a man as all the little people of the world faced their overbearing masters. His resistance burgeoned from every pore of his skin. This boy's face seemed to me most extraordinarily beautiful not only because of the temper smouldering in his eyes but because of the bone structure of his face, the thunderous quality of the level brows and square forehead, the sallowness of the skin that set off the gleaming tiger quality of his eyes; because of his beautiful well-shaped head and his long aboriginal hands and legs; his narrow flat feet. I saw now that it was not Spaniard that was in Angus, but the blood of the oldest Australians. From them came the dark eyes and the darkening under the skin. From his Scottish ancestors came the narrow bridged nose and the bone structure of his face and head. God alone knew from whence came his temper. Yet for all his raggedness he was so beautiful to my eyes now that I was overwhelmed with the knowledge. I looked at him and my heart turned to water. I knew that whatever offence Caesar ever committed there would never come punishment from me.

I knew too that I no longer rebelled against my imprisonment and against the tedium and irritating responsibility of teaching children. I did not hear the words of admonishment delivered to Caesar by the head teacher or pay any further attention as he left the room and made his way back to the school. I stood looking at the boy. And he looked back at me.

"Come over here, Caesar." He came towards me warily. I took him by one shoulder and turned him a little so that his face lifted to mine and I could see it clearly. Slowly I marked the contours, so beautifully proportioned, the thick sensual lips, the long childish lashes, the eyes so profoundly rebellious.

I looked at him for a long time. Then I pushed back his hair from his forehead, and I sighed.

"That's all, Caesar," I said.

He looked at me puzzled. Then his eyes dropped slowly to the floor. They came up again swiftly to try and catch me off guard.

"What do you want me to do, miss?" he said reluctantly.

I pulled myself together and shook myself.

"It's a terribly hot day," I said. "I think you mentioned it first, Caesar."

"Uh huh," he agreed.

"Well, let's get on with running this class," I said. "And look, Caesar, if you get into trouble with the head teacher, that's your business. But don't get me into trouble, see?"

"Okay, miss," he said. "Now where do we start with the kids? What they got to draw first?"

At midday it was one hundred and fifteen in the shade. Two children developed what Caesar called "Blood noses" and he went home, against regulations, to his people's place to get enough clean rags to deal with the situation. The children were placed prostrate on the benches of the playground shelter shed and Caesar remained with them to minister to their wants. Periodically I looked out of the pavilion window to see that all was well. Caesar was in varying attitudes. One moment he was on the roof of the shed gazing away to the north hoping to see something of the fire. He stood, his feet apart, his hands on his hips, his dark silhouette sentinel against the thunderous sky. I marvelled at my own naïveté in not having recognised his aboriginal origin. His body had in it the still

307

watchfulness of the black man gazing from his desert look-out across vast oceans of space.

Another moment Caesar was doing involved hand-springs on the floor of the shed for the entertainment of his patients.

For a long time I had had an uneasy feeling that something was wrong. There was a profound sensation of eeriness. Were we, in this school, the last and lonely survivors of a civilisation that once had dwelt in the valley? The day didn't belong to earthly experience. The heat was annihilating, the pall of smoke hung low over everything and the silence was occult.

I went out to the shed to see how the "blood noses" were progressing.

"Caesar," I said, "does this sort of thing often happen in Stirling?"

"Once, about two years ago they had to blow four whistles," he said. "But mostly it's only one or two whistles."

"It's so dark . . . and so still . . ." I said.

Caesar looked at me, heavy with scorn.

"It's 'cause the mill's stopped," he said. "They've 'll gorn to the fire."

My fantasy dreaming of an occult world!

308

Oh heavens, and it was only that the mill had stopped!

Now I knew why the people of Stirling got used to the sound of the mill and were only distressed when it stopped. The mill was not only the wage earner for the town, it was the sound of life itself.

Fortunately the end of the day came.

By four o'clock the temperatures had dropped rapidly and people were trickling back through the town. It was like a race of Negroes coming home from a funeral. All were black and all were tired. It was almost dark, however, before the last of the children was disposed of for the night. We had learned by this time the true extent of the fire. It had swept through three major farms where the northern end of the valley opened out on to the wheat plain. All the stories were of devastated paddocks, fences razed to the ground, hayricks smouldering heaps of cinders, cows rounded up and shot because they couldn't get through the fire, of only one homestead destroyed but of outbuildings completely devastated on the three farms.

Caesar and I walked slowly and wearily back

309

towards the town. We sat down on the mill bridge and stared into the muddy trickle of mid-summer river water.

I took out a cigarette and started to smoke it. Caesar looked at me hungrily.

"I smoke me dad's butts," he said.

"'Strue," he said. "Me dad used to lamm me when he caught me smokin'. He couldn't cure me so he chucks the butts at me when he's finished."

"And you think I'm going to give you my butt?" I said.

"Mightn't be a bad idea," he said.

"Look, Caesar," I said. "I don't mind you smoking butts. I couldn't stop you if I tried, could I? But I'm not going to do something here in the dark and on the sly that I wouldn't do in the middle of day. And in the middle of the day I couldn't give you the butt of a cigarette. Do you know why?"

"Well, why?"

"Because I'd get the sack. No other reason at all."

"Streuth," he said. He sat kicking his bare feet against the wooden horizontals of the bridge. As if by magic and at the command of the genii a man walking across the bridge threw his partly finished cigarette towards

310

the river. The butt, glowing like a tiny comet, hit the railing and fell on to the wooden planks. Caesar, like a nocturnal dragon-fly, darted across the bridge, retrieved the butt and was back in his place beside me.

We sat and smoked in peace. It seemed that all was well with the world.

But when I reached the boarding-house there was a telephone message from Perth waiting for me. Mother was ill and Mary thought I had better come home.

It seemed as if, faint and far away, I heard a knocking at the door.

5

AT "FORTY-FIVE"

THE next day I went to Perth.

I burst into "Forty-five" nearly sick with anxiety and found Mother in the front room, looking very hale and hearty, busily packing her suit-case. Around her the family alternately stormed or sat in some kind of silent and inexplicable dolour.

"Well, I like that!" I said looking at Mother. "I thought you were ill!"

"Not really at all," she said lightly. "Mary had no right to send you a message. It's a mere nothing. I very nearly didn't mention it at all, only I didn't know how I could go to hospital without your discovering it."

"Discovering what? What do you want to go to hospital for, Mama?"

"Just a small lump, dear. I'll have it out and be done with it."

"A small lump!" I said.

Vicky spoke with asperity.

"Now don't you come in upsetting

312

Mother. It's the smallest lump you ever saw. Nothing at all to be worried about."

"Nothing at all to be worried about," said Mother gaily as she folded one more garment and put it in her suit-case. "Now what have I forgotten, I wonder?"

A small lump! Dear God, what did that mean? I was reared in a generation that had a neurosis about *lumps*.

"Where is this lump, Mama?" I asked calmly. I took out a cigarette and hoped no one would notice how my hand trembled.

"It's in the breast, it's not at all unusual, dear. Probably just a cyst and the best thing is to have it out and be done with. Mary got you down because she thought you'd be upset if you were left out of anything. After all, I never *have* been to hospital before. And you know, Theodora, you would have sulked and made it very unpleasant for everybody if we hadn't given you a good excuse to come to Perth."

"You read me like a book," I said. "Well, thanks for the lump, Mama, it does give me a chance of a break. The heat in Stirling was nearly killing me."

Mary was looking at me with her queer dogged look. My thanks for the lump was a trifle over-doing it, she thought. Her eyes were challenging me to give one hint of fear or anxiety. Or any more facetious remarks.

In my mind I was thinking of lumps with terror.

Not *that*! Dear God, not *that*! Not to Mother. What has she done in life that this should be visited on her? Please, let it be just a *lump* and not *that*!

"Who's going to put the kettle on?" I said looking round. Gerry jumped up from the stool beside Mother's case.

"I will," she said. "In moments of need the Montgomerys always send for tea!"

"Better than Irish whiskey," I said with a touch of bitterness to my memory. Everyone laughed hilariously as if a clever joke had been cracked. Our laughter had a hollow sound.

"It's a funny thing," Mother said putting a new hot-water bottle in her case. "We always seem to drink tea when anything important happens."

"Do you remember when Denney ran away?" I said brightly. "I made three lots of tea in three-quarters of an hour."

"And the night your father came home ill. You were only a little girl, Theodora, but you

314

went into the kitchen and lit the wood stove and brought in a cup of tea to me and Tim Riley."

Mother straightened her back and looked vacantly into space.

"If only Tim Riley were here," she said sadly. "We did so many things together in those days. We could have gone through this thing together too."

"Pshaw, Mama!" I said. "You don't have to pull poor Tim Riley back from the grave just to lug a lump out for you. He'd call that downright inconsiderate."

We laughed again, too loudly and too heartily.

"Has anyone heard from Denney?" Mother said looking round innocently.

"Don't pull that one on me, Mama," I said. "I know, if the others don't, that you've been writing to Denney and sending her things too."

"What, me?" said Mother with an air of outraged innocence. "I have done nothing of the kind. There have been one or two short notes . . . just acknowledgments. of letters Denney's written. You needn't think I'm going to forgive her so easily. I've washed my hands of Denney."

"Stuff and nonsense!" I said. "Anyhow she'll be here next week and we'll see about the hand washing then."

They all looked at me in surprise.

"Next week? What for?"

"Tonsils. She wants to see a doctor about having them out."

It was a blatant lie. I just knew if this thing of Mother's was serious Denney would have to be told. Her appearance wouldn't unduly alarm Mother if I forecast it.

Gerry brought in the tea and we hailed it as if she had produced a feast.

"Wonderful tea," Mother said. "Funny how it relieves one of all one's pains and aches. Worries too."

I wasn't fooled. Mother's eyes were hard and bright and right in their depths was a lurking fear. She had been a nurse all her life. She knew what lumps in the breast meant.

We began to tell silly stories and forced anecdotes of our various lives. We reminded Mother of the day she had gone to see Mary perform in a swimming carnival and of her terror when she saw Mary mount the high dive. Mother hadn't known that Mary could dive at all. She had buried her face in her hands and begged us piteously to tell her

316

when the dive was over. She couldn't bear to watch. There had been a splash and a burst of applause and Mother between parting fingers had asked—

"Is it all over?"

And Denney had replied.

"Yes, but she hasn't come up . . . yet."

Mother had moaned and then when Mary's black bob of a head appeared above the water we had all shouted and clapped our hands. Then Mother was so furious with us she pretended we didn't belong to her.

We reminded her of the day when she and Denney met Gerry in the street and Gerry had Denney's skirt on.

"Take off my skirt at once," Denney had almost danced in her rage. Gerry had calmly taken off the skirt and walked home in her petticoat.

We laughed loudly as we recounted the old stories of our sorrows and our joys but behind the laughter there were tears in all our voices, and beyond the bragging there was terror in every one of us.

Bill Jennings arrived with an awful clash and rattle of tinware. He had borrowed an old Ford from one of his journalist friends and he insisted on taking Mother to hospital.

We made more tea and told more stories. Bill had some of his own to add. Beneath it all we were whimpering like frightened children.

She told us the story of the argument she had had with the young man in the bank because he wouldn't transfer her savings account to a cheque book account.

"You shouldn't have said 'transfer,' Mama," I said. "You used the wrong word. You should have said you were going to 'open a current account.' Then you could have transferred your money."

"Theodora's going to *teach* us our banking business now she's become a school-ma'am," said Gerry.

I looked at Bill beseechingly.

"It's the horn-rimmed glasses, Theodora," he said shaking his head.

I took them off. Mama's face blurred a minute then I could see her wiping the tears of laughter out of her eyes as she recollected the young bank officer's face when she scolded him and finally stalked off to find the manager.

"Put on your glasses, Theodora," Mother said. "Without them you look a little vague, and I'm sure that you really have got brains."

I didn't want to look as if I had brains. I

318

resolutely put my glasses in my pocket.

It was all pointless, inane, and a little brave . . . this way we talked at one another. We had to be brave.

They went away gaily. The Ford chutting and rattling, Gerry and Vicky laughing and giving the driver advice. Mother waving her hand merrily and calling out blithely that she'd see us in the morning.

I stood at the gate and watched them banging, clattering, laughing down the street. Mother's hand was still waving as they turned the corner.

Not all the pageantry of kings and empires made so noble or so touching an exit.

Gerry had sent Denney a telegram and when the surgeon came out of the theatre in the morning he was faced with five Montgomerys, their faces white with anxiety.

"Take it easy, girls," he said wearily. "Take it easy!"

He'd been shut up in that theatre with our mother for two and a half hours. We knew it was no "little lump."

"The worse first," he said, standing there

in the corridor. "I amputated the breast. It was a malignant growth."

Gerry began to cry.

"Shut up," said Mary savagely.

"Cancer!" said Denney. She staggered a little on her feet and her hand clutched my arm.

"When you've digested that, I'll tell you the best," the surgeon said quietly.

"It was a small growth in the primary stage. I removed the whole breast as a precaution. There is no vestige of the growth left. I cannot say it will not recur but I do say that, having got it at this stage, recurrence is unlikely. Your mother has a good chance, as good a chance as any of you, of lasting a normal lifetime."

He began to take out a cigarette slowly. My knees shook so that I had to lean against the wall. The surgeon lit his cigarette and looked at us through trailing smoke.

"There's going to be a psychological shock for your mother," he said. "Cancer is a thing that once faced ceases to be so terrifying. But mutilation is something every woman, no matter what age, finds herself unable to face for a long time."

The horror of that operation dawned on

me. A woman's breast? Yes, it was part of her being, part of her feminine nature. I thought with terror of Mother having to divest herself of clothes in the bathroom and be faced with that terrible wound.

"It's up to you girls," the surgeon said.

We nodded dumbly. Some of us tried to thank him. He walked away down the corridor, tall, thin, tired.

Gerry began to sob bitterly.

"Shut up," said Mary between stiff white lips.

"Oh, leave her alone," said Denney. "Nobody'd expect *you* to understand what Gerry and I feel. We're the only ones who really love Mother. All you think about is your law and your distinctions and the big I-am you are down there at the University."

"*You* love Mother," said Mary. All the bitterness against Denney's run-away marriage seethed up in her now. "All you've ever done to show your love has been to bring shame on her."

I felt too sick to do anything about the quarrel. I knew that it arose from nerves strained to breaking point.

"Miss Legal-Smarty," said Denney insolently. She seemed common and cheap in that rejoinder and Mary seeing it turned away and walked rapidly down the corridor.

"Now see what you've done," said Vicky. "And everyone in the hospital can hear you going on. Thank God Mother's unconscious and doesn't know. *Awful creatures!*"

"Mind your own business," said Denney. There was a chair in the corner of the hall and she sat down on it suddenly and wept bitterly. Gerry hunched against the wall near her and the tears flowed like rain down her face.

I thought if I didn't go outside I'd be sick. I wondered where I could go and vomit in decency and privacy.

If the righteous, when sick and ailing, deserve the ministering touch of an angel from heaven, then Mother was indeed righteous and the angel did indeed hover about her night and day. The angel came disguised as Denney.

"I could not believe that anyone in all the world could be so good and kind," Mother said.

Denney sat with her day and night. She fed her, brought her flowers and books and chocolates and fruit. She washed and laundered her clothes and wrote her letters. She entertained her through her waking hours and watched over her, a relentless watch-dog, while she slept.

Whatever the rest of us did for Mother was only by Denney's gracious permission. To get to Mother's bedside without Denney's watchful and proprietorial eye was almost a physical impossibility. If any one of us offered to wash a night-gown for Mother, Denney took it as an insult to her own efforts. If we brought chocolates and fruit Denney brushed them away as unnecessary. She had provided.

Only Mary was left out in the cold.

Mary was long-suffering by nature. She had a rigid sense of obligation and duty and she had a patience, a discipline and consistency of effort in relation to her work that not one of the rest of us had. She also had a high sense of decorum which we all offended again and again. But she forgave and endured. Nevertheless, there came times when she had had all that she was prepared to endure. And as far as Denney was concerned this was one of them.

Denney's final remark in the corridor on the day of Mother's operation was the last of

323

a long line of such remarks. Mary walked out of the hospital and would only come to see Mother when she was certain that Denney wasn't there. And that wasn't very often.

When Mother went back to "Forty-five" to convalesce Mary wouldn't stay in the house if Denney were there. As for John, Denney's husband, Mary passed him in the street as she would pass a stranger.

We had time now to look at Denney and see what marriage had done for her. She had filled out and where she had looked a somewhat delicate willowy creature she now seemed robust with health. She and John were an odd couple. They seemed to speak rarely to one another in the presence of the family. They spoke *of* one another as if the other weren't present. Yet they went everywhere together. If Denney went out to make one of the interminable cups of tea we consistently drank, John got up quietly from his seat and went too. We called them "me and my shadow." They were happy in their queer undemonstrative way.

John remained indifferent to the Montgomerys as a family. He neither liked nor disliked us. He was not amused by us and he was not bored. He didn't favour us with enough interest even to dislike us.

What Mother endured in her own mind during those first few months we could only guess. Once she told me that sometimes she woke in the night, when a person feels most alone in the world, and the realisation hit her like a stunning blow on the head. She only ever mentioned it once.

In a short time, almost too short to be believed, she was back at her old business of running a family, a house and a job. The colour came back to her face and health revived her strong purposeful walk. She made a joke about her false bust. The only thing she couldn't get over and for which she couldn't forgive us, was that a permanent family rift had occurred.

"I daren't even go to hospital but you're at one another like a lot of Kilkenny cats."

"It'll blow over, Mama," I said. But Mother knew our Mary and sadly shook her head.

"It's a good job I didn't die," she said. "You probably would have murdered one another over my grave.

"Or maybe if I had died, it would have punished you all into silence."

"Oh, for God's sake, Mama," I cried. "Don't talk like that."

"You were the eldest, Theodora, not counting Vicky who I know was *very* upset. You ought to have known better than let them quarrel."

Mother looked at me and shook her head.

"I expect it will take a marriage or a death in the family to unite us again."

"Let us hope it will be a marriage," I said.

Even cancer couldn't keep Mother down.

"If I'd been there, I'd have boxed all your ears," she said. She was there, all right, and that was why we had quarrelled. We'd been afraid.

"Theodora, *will* you put your glasses on," Mother said.

"No, Mama, I won't," I said. "They make me look like a school-teacher."

6

THE WELCOME

AFTER Mother's operation I persuaded the Education Department to transfer me to a town school. I was needed at home. The depression was setting in and funds were low.

On my last day at Stirling school Caesar brought me a bunch of flowers. They were bedraggled and of weedish origin; they drooped, their stems were too short and they were ill-mixed. But it was a most beautiful present.

Through the pavilion window I had seen Caesar coming down the street, a small posse of children milling about him but keeping a safe distance; and in his hand was this crude bunch of flowers. Caesar was always the first to annihilate with derisive laughter the sissies who brought the teacher flowers. He came down the street now casting murderous looks at his escort, periodically making sorties in the direction of those who annoyed him most, but still clinging to that bunch of flowers.

When he reached the school-gates the numerical strength of his body-guard increased considerably.

He stood glowering at me, the old "stick-a-knife-in-your-heart" look on his face. He held out the flowers as one might hold out an asp.

I took them and said nothing. Sentimental thanks would have killed the thing that was between us. But I stood looking at him, and the children, oddly and instinctively perceptive, faded away.

For a long time we looked at one another and then Caesar began to kick the floor with his foot. His head drooped a little.

"Will you give out the pads and pencils?" I asked.

His head jerked up and he hitched his pants.

"Okay, miss," he said. He began to bound about the room like a monkey, dark, saturnine, mischievous.

When I left the school in the afternoon I took the flowers with me, and when I went to the train later in the evening the flowers came too. I knew that I would see Caesar somewhere before the train went out.

Sure enough he appeared on the railway line on the side away from the platform. This was dangerous and against the law, but Caesar was no abider of the law. He stood looking at me with a sly grin, his black eyes gleaming, his feet planted apart.

I waited until the train whistled and then I leaned out of the window.

"Here, Angus," I said. "From me to you." I gave him my cigarette-case, full of cigarettes, and a box of matches.

I had called him "Angus" instinctively. I felt that parting dignified for him a name already great in the annals of history. The cigarettes were for Caesar, the gutter-snipe; but the name was for Angus, an ideal not to be sneered at.

In Perth the depression closed about us like a wet blanket. Teaching became arduous and dispiriting. The crusading spirit was wounded near unto death by the lack of equipment, over-crowded classes and the machine product that was the highest ideal of education as interpreted by the "old hands."

I struggled with this part of my life desperately and only because of necessity. On all except rare occasions my job became merely the means of collecting a pay envelope.

I tried to bury my stricken conscience in the Book.

"How's it going?" Sam asked me quietly.

"It goes slowly," I said. "Why didn't you tell me it takes so long to write a book? I've been over a year on it now and I'm not a third of the way through."

"What's happened to all those words of yours?"

"Oh, they come out by the thousand sometimes. Then I think of another and better way of writing the same thing, and a few more thousand come. Then there are times when not one word will come. Nothing comes from the pen but blobs of watery, depression ink."

"You should have a typewriter," he said.

The next day he brought me an old machine that he picked up in a second-hand shop, and a Pitman's typewriting instructor.

"Leave the Book alone for a while," he said. "Every tradesman should have his tools and you must learn to use a typewriter."

Sometimes he dropped in after dinner at night to see how I was progressing. We sat on the edge of my bed on the balcony room and discussed typing exercises. Mother was sure it was not quite nice, but at the moment her thoughts were chiefly taken up with Vicky and a rising young business man who was interested in music and was taking Vicky to concerts.

I came home from school one afternoon and when I brought the tea in I noticed that Mother sat over her embroidery more thoughtfully silent than usual.

"What's up?" I said.

"What do you think of David Browning?" she countered.

"I hardly know him," I said. "But he seems all right. Vicky likes him."

"And he likes Vicky. He came at lunch-time to see if I would give my approval to their becoming engaged."

"Oh, Mama! Our Vicky engaged! How much dough has he got? Vicky could never earn a decent living for herself!" The three of us earning, Mother, Vicky and myself, had had depression cuts of twenty per cent in our salaries. And the genteel school had paid barely a living allowance before.

"Quite a lot, it seems," Mother said. "Also a fine house his parents left him and a large motor-car."

"Snap him up, Mama," I said. "Catch him, leg-rope and halter."

She looked at me angrily.

"That's you all over, Theodora," she said. "Not a word about whether he's suitable for Vicky. Whether he will make her happy or not."

"Oh nuts! Mama. Vicky'll be happy any place where there's a nice comfortable nest and someone with time and money to pet her. That's all Vicky needs in life."

Mother looked at me with real anger.

"You've never understood Vicky," she said. "Now I believe that you've always been jealous."

"Jealous my hat! Look, Mama, all I care about Vicky is that she's found someone who can give her the kind of life you and the Bastons have reared her for. Vicky's never had to stand up to anything, even a headache. When things have gone wrong she's always had you and Mrs. Baston, but someday you'll both be dead. Who's going to look after Vicky then? You don't suppose that 'Genteel' School is going to pay her a pension when she's too old to be any further use? If David Browning is decent and on the level, grab him. For goodness' sake, Mama, throw your hat in the air. She's darned lucky. With David Browning Vicky's got a career handed out to her on a platter and wrapped in silver paper."

Mother had put down her sewing and was looking at me with serious eyes.

"You're very cynical, Theodora."

"I'm twenty-four and getting on for spinsterhood. Anyhow, as far as being jealous of Vicky is concerned, I just can't tell you how glad I am that someone like David Browning has turned up. I was dead scared it might be me who would have to spend my declining years taking her her aspirin and putting hot-water bottles in her bed."

"You're a wicked girl, Theodora," said Mother. "And you've got a bitter tongue."

"It's not bitter. It's truthful."

"Go and put the kettle on," she said. "It's time the others were in and they'll need their tea. And Theodora! Put your glasses on or I'll feel like slapping you."

Vicky and David wanted to be married within three months so we called them "royalty" and set about preparing a wedding. Once Mother had accepted Vicky's imminent departure as a fact, the only cloud in her sky was that Vicky didn't want to be a beautiful bride. She just wanted a small wedding and

333

insisted on wearing a plain dress with a flowery hat and carrying a Prayer Book instead of a sheaf of flowers. Mother, still dreaming of the days when Vicky had been a spangling fairy at the Baston weddings, swallowed her disappointment hard.

When Vicky went to the altar Mother shed tears, not because her eldest child was going from the home but for the trailing wedding dress, the misty veil, and the waterfall of flowers that Vicky spurned.

The family sat in divided camps on either side of the church. Even a wedding hadn't united it.

"That's two of you gone," Sam said to me. "Who's next?"

He looked at me quizzically. "How are you and Paul getting on these days? And I seem to have heard something of that wild Irishman being up from the bush last holidays."

"Both time and water have flowed under the bridge since Paul and I were engaged," I said sententiously. "And as for Paddy, he's got another blonde, a sister of the one he had the year before last. I love them both, Sam," I said with mock sorrow. "But they'll have nought of me."

"Paul really is going to England at the end of the year?"

"Yes, and I don't think he'll come back."

"Well, supposing you and I do a little walking out?" he said with a grin.

I took his arm affectionately.

"I'd love to. When do we start?"

"To-night. Come home with me and meet my people."

"Why, Sam, I'd love to. But do you know what . . . I'd never thought of you as having people. You always seem such a lone wolf."

"I've got people all right. We'll go home and have dinner with them."

"But they're not expecting us."

"That won't matter. My father and mother are Quakers, by the way. Quakers always keep open houses. And listen, Theodora . . . do you think you could sneak down the garden-path to have that cigarette of yours?"

Sam had actually gone pink.

"Of course, Sam," I said. "Do they think smoking is very wicked?"

"No. I smoke myself. But I'd like the first impression to be the best. Do you mind? They wouldn't really care at all if you smoked . . . it's just that they wouldn't think of you as one of themselves."

I cocked a puzzled eye at him. Who, I wondered, wanted them to think of me as one of themselves? I decided the subject was delicate and now was not the time to ask Sam.

When I entered the Richardson home it was like entering another world. The kind of world I'd read about, even seen in plays and films, but not the kind of world in which I really believed.

Sam led me into a large square living-room where a low fire was burning in the grate. On either side of this fire there sat two figures. One of them rose. He was a tall slender man, white-haired and with an aura of apostolic saintliness about him. There was something so good and clean and gentle about him, something so other-worldly that I was quite nonplussed. For a moment I thought I had stumbled on a character out of the Bible, and because when I discover these new things in life I have to stand and stare I forgot my manners for a minute and hesitated before I took his out-stretched hand.

Then I saw that the hand, slender, long and white, was fumbling a little in the air. I realised that he, the owner of the hand, was blind.

My voice choked a little as I shook hands and said, "How-do-you-do."

"You are welcome, my child," he said. He felt my hand with the two of his.

"This is my brother, Jim," said Sam. I turned to the other figure sitting by the fire. The young man who had not risen. Then I saw that his chair was no ordinary chair. It was a wheel-chair. Over his legs there was stretched a rug.

Jim placed his spectacles in the fold of his book and held out his hand.

I went over to him and saw that I did not have to pity him. He had Sam's strong scholarly face but something more in it. A certain peacefulness and a certitude of his own well-being.

"What are you reading?" I asked as we shook hands.

"*Oliver Twist*," he said. "Do you read Dickens?"

"I used to," I said apologetically. "I haven't read anything of his for a long time. I'm afraid I'm rather wedded to the moderns at the moment."

"We are always reading Dickens in this house," put in Mr. Richardson's grave voice. "That is until I completely lost my sight. Jim reads to me now."

The lame leading the blind!

Presently I got over the lump in my throat and began to realise that there was something safe and secure in this room. The men spoke quietly together and with great dignity. As each spoke the others listened acutely and presently their voices would take up the thread of the conversation. I sat mute, listening without hearing. Then I was aware of someone stirring outside the further door and Sam got up and opened it.

"Come in, Mother," he said. Mrs. Richardson came forward looking at me with wondering shy eyes.

"You are welcome, my child," she said.

I had an insane desire to giggle. I didn't think there was anything in the least funny about the scene. I was impressed by tragedy surmounted, by peace and security attained. My desire to giggle was an overburdening of feeling.

Mrs. Richardson was a short, bird-like woman, with quick bird-like movements, and such a simple sincerity shining in her face that I fell her victim at once.

"You do not know all Sam's family," she said gently. "I must show them to you." She brought a huge red leather photograph album out from the lower shelf of one of the occasional tables.

Around the walls were photographs which I identified as Sam's grandparents, resplendent in large oval wooden framed pictures; Mr. and Mrs. Richardson in the bloom of old-fashioned high-collared youth. Sam and Jim, the latter in a wheel-chair; Sam and the younger brother standing sturdily on a stool to reach his bigger brother's shoulder. No foretelling in that straight back and those strong legs of a history, yet to be written, in a wheel-chair. Jim had been stricken with infantile paralysis when he was seven years old.

Mrs. Richardson opened the album.

She pointed to the first of a group of photographs.

"That is a branch of the family in England," she said. "Of course we haven't met for three generations now."

Her bird-like finger pointed to two figures in walrus moustaches.

"That is Cousin George the First," she said. "And the other is Cousin George the Third." I was thinking vaguely of the kings of England.

"How many Cousin Georges are there?" I asked.

"Five," she said.

"George seems to be a family name," I said. "Yet you haven't called either of your sons by it."

"Oh no," said Mrs. Richardson vaguely explanatory. "George is the name belonging to the older branch of the family. The senior branch. Our family name, in our branch, is Samuel."

She looked round proudly.

"And there's my Samuel there," she said. When his mother turned her head back to the album Sam smiled at me and there was the faintest suspicion of a wink in his left eye.

"How many Samuels are there?" I asked weakly.

"Only two," she said. "And our Samuel is the senior. Cousin Samuel the Second lives in Adelaide. He's quite well acquainted with the family of Cousin George the Fifth."

What was I to do? Why hadn't Sam prepared me for his family? Did he just know that I would be moved by their kindness and their sincerity?

"Do you think Cousin Theodora would like a cup of tea?" Mr. Richardson asked in a gentle voice.

I started. I looked at Sam beseechingly. I

340

hadn't been promoted to the family already surely?

Sam was smiling at me with real amusement. He sat back in his low chair, one hand on his knee and one hand in his pocket. His blue-grey eyes were twinkling. He was aware of my dilemma and understood the impact of his family on me.

"Sam," I said accusingly. "Haven't you brought a girl home before?"

"Oh yes," Mrs. Richardson put in quickly. "He used to bring Ellie Hamilton here often. Father, you didn't call her 'cousin' did you?"

I felt appreciatively "snooty" about this Ellie Hamilton. She hadn't been promoted to cousinship in spite of several visits. This was my first.

"Why did you call me 'cousin', Mr. Richardson?" I asked. "Does it mean you approve of Sam knowing me?"

I was surprised at my own anxiety to hear words of approval—from his gentle lips.

"Sam has spoken of you often," he said. "We wondered when he would bring you home."

Bring me home! I looked at Sam with dismay and suspicion. Had Sam brought me *home*?

I got up suddenly and stood in front of the photograph of his grandparents. I couldn't see it for the mist in my eyes. I wished I'd put my spectacles on, I thought lamely. I can't see properly without them.

They must all have sensed how mixed my feelings were for they sat silent for a moment. Then Mr. Richardson spoke again.

"You are welcome, my child," he said.

Oh Sam! Don't you understand?

I've no place here. I'm lost and a stranger. My feet would trample this garden too. Just as I trampled Paul's garden. I talked too much and too vehemently for this house of angels. I don't belong.

Sam came across the room and put his arm around my shoulder.

"My father would like you to know you are welcome here, Theodora. Welcome to come and go."

I understood his meaning.

I went across to Mr. Richardson and took his hand.

"Thank you," I said. He patted my hand.

"What about a cup of tea, Mother?"

Jim craned his neck around the corner of his chair.

"Mother looked after the two children in

the opposite house to-day," he said. "And what do you think? They kept running down the street so she tied up the gate. They stood there and watched her solemnly tying up the gate and then they asked her why. 'To keep you from running away,' she told them. 'But we don't go through the gate,' young Johnny said. 'We go over the fence'."

We all laughed.

He had deliberately told the little story and when Mrs. Richardson came in with the tea we sat around the fire and drank it and talked about Dickens.

When Sam took me home as far as the gate of "Forty-five" I leaned against him. I felt so good and his arm seemed so safe.

"Like Niobe, all tears," he said stroking my hair.

Then he kissed me. The extraordinary thing was I felt ants crawling down my spine.

I went to bed puzzled. I was sure I wasn't in love with Sam but I couldn't account for those ants.

My sensations with Paddy had been purely primitive. This was more delicate and subtle.

And not at all improper.

7

THE WAY HOME

MARY went to the Bar, clad in austere, forbidding, and legal splendour.

It was hard to recognise her under the long black gown and the white curled wig. Her face was taut and white and her trembling fingers clutched tightly the significant scroll.

It was funny, I thought, how none of the Montgomerys, for all their arrogance and versatility of tongue, could ever face up to a public appearance. We turned white at the gills and trembled so obviously that it filled the bystanders with consternation and embarrassment.

Mother, Vicky and I sat in silence watching the formal ceremony and were impressed by the solemn dignity of the tributes to Mary made to the Full Court Judges by Mary's Principal. It was only at that moment, though I had seen the sacrifice and toil of years as an eye-witness, I realised to what goodly heights

Mary had battled her way in the world of sceptical men. It seemed to me to be profoundly moving that this man, her Principal—one whose hair had grown white with honours in the legal profession—should be presenting Mary to the Bar as an honoured and esteemed colleague.

Mother sat, stiff with pride. The only cloud in her sky on this day, which she felt marked the ascendency out of the pit for the Montgomery family, was the deliberate absence of Denney and Gerry.

"Mary's put us back on the map again," Mother said nodding her head and biting her under-lip thoughtfully.

"Which map, Mama?" I asked.

"Now, Theodora," she said angrily. "Don't you attempt to detract from Mary's achievement. She's done something few girls can do, even with all the advantages of security. She's got brains and she's struggled. She's got there and she's taken us all with her. Just you mind that edge on your tongue to-day, or I'll give you both sides of mine."

"I wouldn't detract from Mary one whit," I said with docility. "I admire her. And I envy her too. . . . I wish I'd done what she's done. But Mama . . . about that map? You

345

don't mean the *social* map, I hope? Hasn't the behaviour of all your old Pepper Tree Bay friends, with the solitary exception of the Bastons, told you what that's worth? If that's what you and Mary have been struggling for, why then you've got all your values wrong."

"That's Socialist talk," Mother said severely. By that she meant a watering down of Communism.

Mary was being photographed by the Press outside the Court.

"That'll make the men hate her," I said. "The legal men, I mean. They'll call it cheap advertisement and tell bawdy tales about her."

"Oh that tongue of yours, Theodora!" Mother said desperately. "Must you spoil everything for me?"

"I'm sorry," I said contritely. It wasn't only a sharp tongue that I had but a sharp and seeing eye. I never could make myself believe Mother really wanted to have the wool pulled over her eyes. But she did. She wanted to believe that Mary's colleagues were thrilled with astonishment and admiration at her success. She thought they too would pore over her photographs in the newspapers, add up how much more difficult her job had been because of their masculine obstruction, then cluck their tongues and wonder afresh at Mary's rise to fame. For fame it was, since there had only been one woman in Western Australia who had ever got as far as the Bar. On this day Mary was one of four, but Mother had no eyes for the others. In her pride it seemed to her that Mary alone achieved this distinction.

"Denney and Gerry should have come," she said. "It was mean and little of them to carry their animosity so far."

Gerry had joined forces with Denney in the tribal feud rending the family. Gerry, always with an eye to the advantage of being dif ferent, had found the rest of us unendurable and sought Denney's entertainment and com- panionship. She found it quite profitable from the point of view of freedom to have a still-young married sister upon whom she could periodically cast herself. Denney and John had come to live in Perth and were in a street scarce a quarter of a mile from "Forty- five."

"A marriage hasn't brought you girls together," Mother had said. "I guess I'll have to die to manage that."

"Mama, if you say that again I'll leave the house for ever," I said.

"If only they'd been here," Mother said shaking her head.

"Oh get in the car and stop worrying," Vicky said. She was looking like a million dollars in her wide furs, her beautifully shod feet, and her immaculately gloved hands.

"Nice to be Vicky," I thought. I leaned back and enjoyed her car.

She drove us to the hotel where we were to celebrate with a luncheon.

Sam and Bill Jennings together with a number of Mary's friends from the University and legal world met us in the foyer. Mary had got over her nervousness and, outside the legal regalia, she looked feminine and bewitching. She walked about with a cloud of young men trailing around her.

"The pity of it is this," I said to Sam in an aside. "She'll get married now and all that work will be wasted."

"Surely not," said Sam jingling the money in his pockets. "Brains and training are never wasted."

"You don't know your Australian male," I said. "Why any Australian man goes into the Hall of Learning to get his wife I do not know. He really should go to the scullery."

He looked at me and raised one eyebrow.

"How's the Book going?" he said.

"It isn't," I said. "That's the trouble. I've bogged down."

He smiled at me.

"You're suffering from writer's depression," he said. "I believe they all get it."

"Truly?"

"Absolutely truly."

I squeezed his arm.

"I'd hate to believe I'm jealous and I can't believe I really am," I said, "but somehow Mary's achievement fills me with a sense of my own frustration. I feel such a hopeless dill myself."

"You're a trained teacher. That's something you've achieved."

"What an achievement!" I said bitterly. "I'm a failure at it. Anyone with a flair for kids and without one atom of training could make a better go of it than I do under the present system."

He looked at me speculatively and then he said—

"I'd get on with the Book if I were you, Theodora."

I looked at him wonderingly. Presently he stirred.

"Why do you look at me like that?" he asked.

349

I blinked my eyes and shook my head.

"I don't see very well, that's all."

"Why don't you wear your spectacles?"

"I don't *have* to wear them except for reading," I said a little shame-faced and not quite truthfully. "I don't care much for them," I added quickly.

Sam went on looking at my face for a long time. Then he laughed and squeezed my hand.

"Don't ever wear glasses, Theodora," he said.

"But, Sam, I *must*—sometimes."

He shook his head and laughed.

"Mary, Mary, quite contrary."

"But it's you that's contrary—" I said, a little bewildered.

We dined and wined Mary and then went home feeling replete and a little funny in the head.

"Are you a Quaker yourself, Sam?"

He rubbed his eyes. The thick lashes drooped on his cheek making me feel unduly tender towards him.

"I think some intellectuals outgrow religious sectarianism," he said. "But the training sticks. I can never quite *not* be a

350

Quaker. There are some things I balk at automatically."

"Like telling a lie. You never tell lies, do you Sam? Not even little white ones."

"Don't I?" said Sam looking at me with interest and surprise.

"No. You're the most palpably honest person I've ever known. Perhaps it's because of that the truth from you doesn't hurt."

He went on looking at me in thoughtful surprise.

There was a little silence between us. All of a sudden it became awkward.

"I'm wondering about something too," Sam said.

"Then wonder on till truth makes all things plain."

"I'm wondering if it's the time and the place and the hour?"

Had I heard a phrase like that before? A sudden poignant memory of the arundinaceous places smote me. But Sam would know nothing about places like that!

"What are you talking about?" I asked nervously. I avoided his eyes. "I think I'll make a cup of tea."

Sam gave a burst of laughter. It was a nice baritone musical laugh.

"Somebody's scared," he said.

I laughed and went into the kitchen. I began to feel trembly at the knees.

Sam, I thought, don't ask me to marry you! I don't love you. I ought to love you, because I can't do without you. It fills me with terror to think that you might go away or find someone else. I couldn't bear to give you up. But I know, I just know, that I don't love you.

I heard Sam coming down the passage and I pretended to be fiddling with the automatic lighter on the gas stove. He put one arm around me and I felt the old and wonderful comfort of his nearness. He put the other hand up and turning my head kissed me on the mouth.

"Sam, do you get ants down your spine when you kiss me?"

"Very much so," he said with a grin. "Very much too much so."

"So do I. Would it be a good sign?"

"The best sign I know," he said. "Very important indeed."

I stared at the smoking kettle.

"Go and empty the teapot," I said.

He went out the door. It seemed to me as if his smile was too knowing.

Mother had been lying down and when she

heard the teacups rattling she came outside.

"Mrs. Monty," said Sam from the depths of the arm-chair. "With your permission, I'm going to take your daughter for a walk."

Mother looked at him with a slightly bewildered air. Nobody asked her permission for anything. Why was Sam making such a business of a mere walk?

"A walk?" she said. "Where were you thinking of going?"

"Are you sure I have your permission?" he said smiling.

"I don't know what you're talking about, Sam. As far as I'm concerned you can go for a walk, but Theodora is the most self-willed person. She's not likely to stay home even if I didn't approve of her young men."

"We're going into town," Sam said getting up. "A good brisk walk there and back will improve your daughter's behaviour beyond recognition."

"Why are we going to town?" I asked contrarily. "I don't even like the place."

"I want to see a friend," said Sam. "He has a little shop in the Arcade. I promised him I'd call and see his stuff. Come with me, Theodora? I'll guarantee you'll like it."

"All right," I said after a minute. "But I

353

promise you I'll not say a single word all the way there. I'm too tired to talk."

"Promise accepted," he said.

We put on our glad hats again and solemnly walked the mile into Perth in complete silence. When we came to the Arcade Sam showed me his friend's shop. It was a tiny little jeweller's tucked away in a remote corner.

"Hallo, Sam. I wondered if you were going to turn up." His friend was grinning at him knowingly.

"Hallo, Bill. Have you got the wares? This is the lady in question. Miss Theodora Eileen Montgomery—Mr. Bill Mayford."

I said "Hallo" awkwardly.

Bill produced two tiny boxes from under the counter.

"Sam says they'll fit," he said. "He's been pinching your gloves. Yours is the choice." He flicked open the lids simultaneously and there were two beautiful diamond rings.

"I made 'em myself," said Mr. Bill Mayford, with his wide blue eyes craving admiration. I had the awful feeling that I could let Sam down . . . but not Bill.

"Which is it to be?" said Bill. "You're the lady. It's your choice."

"Well?" said Sam. "Try them on."

354

"Sam . . ." I began accusingly.

"I know . . ." he said. "Which one are you going to wear, Theodora?"

I couldn't think of anything to say. I picked up the rings and put first one and then the other on my finger. I looked up and caught his eyes staring at me intently. They were dark, as if they had pain in them. Then he smiled and it was gone. I felt startled, and afraid to oppose Sam. Not afraid *of* Sam . . . afraid of myself, and of loneliness.

"This one," I said.

We shook hands with Mr. Bill Mayford and said good-bye. Sam smiled into my eyes.

"We'll go and find out about those ants," he said.

I followed him out of the shop and out of the Arcade. He called a taxi and when we were in it Sam leaned across me and pointed to all the people in the street.

"They're just ordinary people," he said. "Living and loving in the ordinary way. They are the people of the world, Theodora." He paused a minute and turned his eyes to mine. "Your mind is all taken up with the business of wild romantic love, isn't it? Or love somewhere spiritually lofty in the clouds. You haven't been able to make up

355

your mind which is the right kind of the two. Isn't that true?"

"Gypsy music or Bach!" I said dreamily.

"So that's it, is it," said Sam. "Paddy Donoghue has had you out at that place at Wanneroo?"

"Have you ever been there?" I asked.

"Yes," said Sam. "Everyone tries it once."

"No good?" I asked him, wonderingly.

"Not for me, Theodora. And not for you— any more."

He lifted up my hand and looked at his ring sparkling on my finger.

"How about trying ordinary love, Theodora?"

"Bread and butter and calico," I said, but I didn't mean it sadly.

"We can always have curry for tea on Wednesdays," said Sam. He squeezed my hand so hard it hurt, and we smiled at one another.

8

GOOD NIGHT

IN the end it was John, Denney's husband, who brought the family together again. John . . . who couldn't have cared less!

Nothing, Mother had said, but a funeral would bring us all together. We had been afraid that it might be her funeral. But it wasn't. It was John's.

He had died in his sleep. One moment he had been working, laughing, joking, big with life; the next he had been lying in his bed, his face benign with peace, his heart still.

No one could have been carried to his last resting-place with greater honour and compassion than that with which we, the Montgomerys, carried John. The strange and poignant part of it was that John probably wouldn't have cared at all. In our broad passionate gestures to heap the honour of affection on him we were only answered by the cold inimical silence of death.

357

There was no one else to take him away and put him in the earth. He had no relatives. In death he was ours.

We were all there at "Forty-five" with Denney. Mother in the kitchen made scones and more tea; Vicky, lying stretching on the floor gently patted Denney's foot. Gerry bathed Denney's eyes with a bowl of warm water on her knee. I, restless, wandered about between the telephone and the front door. Mary went out.

"Where has she gone?" I asked Mother.

"She's gone to fix John's things," Mother said in a whisper. "Denney said to leave everything as it was, but we couldn't do that. We couldn't let her go back to the house and find his things lying about everywhere . . . just as he left them."

My eyes filled with tears.

"Now, Theodora," Mother said turning on me sharply. "There's to be none of that. If Denney can control herself you can."

I looked back into her angry face. She was there towering over us again, the matriarch, the law-giver; and the defence. Against all ills she stood indomitable. To-day was not Denney's or John's day. It was her day. Death had

358

delivered the family again into her hands. She was running us.

It shocked me. What of John? Had Mother never really forgiven him? Didn't it matter that a human being, once full of all the joyous ways of life, lay dead?

My eyes fell away from her fierce gaze.

"Shall I go with Mary?" I asked.

"No," she said. "If you both go Denney will miss you. It's better that Mary put everything away without telling her. Afterwards Denney will be glad."

When she came back she looked exhausted.

"It must have been pretty grim for you," I said.

"I got through it all right," she said. "I washed the clothes he wore yesterday. The woman next door will take them off the line. I felt dull and feelingless most of the time. It was only the little chair . . ." her eyes filled up with tears. "The little chair by the window. It was upside down with the hammer and tacks and webbing beside it. He was working on it when he went to bed. That and the seedlings in the sink. I felt I couldn't do any more after that." Her heart was sick with remorse and the bitter feeling that it was too late to be kind to John.

"Would you like me to go up with you later?"
She nodded.
"After tea," she said.

It was Mary who went to the Royal Perth for the death certificate and who later took it to the coroner. An examination had showed that he died from natural causes . . . coronary thrombosis.

To Denney, more than death itself, was the heart-breaking pity of that last word never spoken.

Mary it was who did all these things for John as if, in her attention to the most painful detail, she could redeem the heart-burning his marriage to Denny had caused her. John in death, cold and silent, could give her no answer.

The rest of us surrounded Denney as if by the full force of our numbers we would make a wall against sorrow.

The door bell rang incessantly and telegrams came in sheaves.

We talked as we had never talked before, Denney's voice rising as with violent gestures she would denounce this and that about the world she had known. With high-pitched over-wrought voices the rest of us gave tongue to our rememberings. We could not be silent. Our pity burgeoned forth from us in torrential words.

We went back over our childhoods. We remembered incidents dug out of the dark unconscious and suddenly thought upon and pounced upon and dragged out into the light for all to see and comment. We remembered people we thought we had forgotten. We remembered terrible things about them; we remembered things so sad about them they would not bear thinking on. We remembered bitter things, and audacious things and our tongues lashed the memory of them.

All the time Denney's voice dominated all.

Then suddenly her eyes would glaze, a look of such horror would crease and curve her whole face that for a moment we all rushed headlong down into the terrible and bottomless pit of sorrow.

Then she would fight back. Out of the pit we would all come crawling after her and the terrible unchecked flow of rememberings would go on.

The people went away as they had come, in ones and twos; their brows clouded and their lips pursed and their eyes astounded because though they could not understand the frightful scene they had witnessed they knew there was valour in us and that our thundering tongues were after all but sad vain protesting anger like that of the angels thrown rebellious from heaven.

Only in the privacy of our own rooms would we admit defeat, admit that there was no defence against death.

The next day, when John was to be buried, Mother and Mary and I took him, in all the trappings of honour, to the graveyard.

"Theodora, I don't think you ought to come," Mother said. "You're too emotional. It'll upset you."

"I'm coming, Mother," I said doggedly. "I wouldn't refuse though the heavens fall."

I didn't tell her, because I was afraid and intimidated by her anger, that I would not let her have John alone for that last hour on earth. She was going to the grave triumphant, righteously inclined to do all that should be done in the matter of putting John away in the earth. If I went I knew there would be one mourner for him and not for Denney. One human being whose heart was heavy with the pity of his death. Mary was filled with her terrible remorse, but that was all.

I was filled with pity for his round strong pleasant face, for the one lock of hair that fell across his forehead, for his deep careless easy voice, for his big strong body that had lifted and moved great weights of the earth yet which had in the end been no stronger than the beat of his heart. I was filled with the awful pity of the fact that he was no more and that only we, aliens, stood around him to say farewell.

I longed for him to know and understand that pity.

I stooped, and taking a card from one of the wreaths, I wrote a line on it and then threw it into the grave. It floated down in the slow up-current of air smelling of the fresh yellow earth. Then it rested on John. It was my last word. I know the affront that Mother suffered as she watched me, and Mary's indignation, but I did not care. It had come from my heart and was for John . . . not for Denney.

"Good night. . . .
And flights of angels wing thee to thy rest."

The first sod of earth fell and pinned it to his breast.

9

HOME AT LAST

FOR a year I worked very hard. I worked at finishing my book and at getting ready to marry Sam.

Sometimes I wondered why I worked so persistently and relentlessly. I worked fourteen hours every day in the week.

I made almost all my clothes for my new life. I embroidered table-cloths and appliqued lace on to silken underwear. I did all the things I thought a girl ought to do and was traditionally expected to do in preparation for her wedding.

My family stood aside and marvelled. They weren't sure my conventional behaviour was quite in character. Maybe it wasn't. Maybe I thought subconsciously that by being good and doing the right thing I would find the way to the pot of gold.

I only went once again, and alone, to hear gypsy music at Wanneroo and it filled me with such a wild intolerable longing I thought there could never be any answer to it on the earth. I never went again.

I taught in a city school all day and when I wasn't teaching, wasn't sewing, wasn't appearing with Sam at the right places, wasn't shopping, I was attacking my book with alternate restlessness, panic and an incoherent fury that I could not write it with time and peace of mind as allies.

Sometimes I put my head in my hands and asked myself what was missing? I had that same sense of an absence that one has when suddenly realising someone is out of the room—someone who, in the inchoate interplay of thought and talk, one cannot for the moment name.

"What is ecstasy, Sam?" I asked. "What things are 'ordinary' people entitled to be ecstatic about?"

He looked at me.

"You're looking for something that's not on the earth, Theodora. It's not real."

"You mean not commonplace?" I said diffidently.

He burst out laughing.

"You're trying very hard, aren't you, darling?"

"I don't know what you mean."

"Never mind, dear. Put it all in your book. That's where it and star-dust belong."

But his eyes were serious and he wasn't laughing at me.

Sometimes I wondered if in seeking I was running away from the thing I sought.

When I had finished the book, not far short of my wedding-day, I could not show it to Sam. I could not get past the fear of showing myself to him. I had undressed the secret places of my heart and they wounded and frightened *me*. What effect would they have on Sam?

In the end he took me to the Professor of English Literature at the University who took the manuscript away and pondered over it for a month.

Then the Professor sent for me.

He looked at me with kindly wise eyes, not amused, over the top of his spectacles.

"You Australians like straight talking," he said. "So I'll speak of this book in your own language. It's so damn' good . . . and so damn' bad."

"It took three years to write," I said humbly, frightened my despair would sound a quaver in my voice.

366

"If you spend another two years on it you will produce something worth while."

"Oh no!" I cried astounded. "I *couldn't* do it."

"It's worth it."

"Two years? It's a lifetime. I *couldn't* do it." I shook my head hopelessly.

His white hands were leafing through the manuscript slowly.

"Several of the passages in it are as good as any I've read . . . anywhere," he said.

I stopped shaking my head and looked at him incredulously.

"That is true," he said. "Your book and your talent are worth while. I believe them to be outstanding. When you can face the fact that the road winds uphill all the way come back and see me. I will help you."

"Uphill all the way?"

"Yes, to the very end."

I got up and went away slowly. I shut the door behind me and was alone in the passage except for my constant, familiar, despair.

"Will the day's journey take the whole long day?
From morn to night, my friend."

A week afterwards I went back and told him I would revise the book.

But beforehand I had to get on with the business of marrying Sam. The primitive had to take precedence over the civilised.

Nobody really approved, with the sole exception of Pat Woods.

She had looked at me speculatively and thought for a long time.

"You know, Theodora," she said. "At the bottom of that muddled pit of thinking which is your excuse for a mind, there's a solid core of common sense. Sam's the only man in the world for you."

Nearly everyone else thought the match was verging on the ridiculous. The exceptions were Sam's people. They had said, "You are welcome, my child," and meant it because I was Sam's choice. Sam was the head of the family!

But others thought differently.

"Don't do it," Paddy wrote from the bush. "Absolutely nothing against Sam. Sam's whitest chap I've ever known . . . stouch anyone who says different. But darlin', it's like the mountain deer bedding down with a giraffe. Intellectually speaking, I mean. They just don't mate."

Paul in the throes of preparing his departure to England was airily indifferent.

My family decided they would believe I would really marry Sam when the wedding invitations were out. Not before. When the wedding invitations were out they said they'd believe it when they saw us together at the altar.

As the wedding-day loomed I realised that Sam stood a good chance of marrying a nervous wreck. I had worked too hard, worried too hard, and been too disappointed when the English professor had bade me put in another two years on my book.

For the preceding weeks I gave myself to another kind of panic, the panic of standing the ordeal of a public performance. Why had I ever dreamed of bridal array? Why had I not realised, when I had agreed to Mother having her way and one of her daughters going to the altar in traditional gown and veil, all that it would involve?

I no longer thought about the book, or what was the true meaning of love. I thought only of getting through the wedding-ceremony without public, abject, and pitiful disgrace.

I no longer even cared about the outrage of giving myself away, body and soul, like a box of necessary tricks. I cared only that I would survive the day with some vestige of pride left.

Sam became only the "other person" for whom it was necessary to be at the church.

I sewed feverishly and stood interminable hours before kneeling dressmakers. I attended afternoon teas and cleared out cupboards, book-shelves and drawers crammed with the collected treasury of many years.

But I couldn't sleep a wink at night. As soon as fatigue dulled my senses to the point of dropping into slumber, my nervous system would let go and I would drop ten inches into spiritual space. I would be desperately awake again, and hideously afraid.

I didn't sleep properly for weeks and as a result my lashing tongue intimidated even the Montgomery family.

And the eve of my wedding-day arrived.

I went into town to have my hair done by the hairdresser. In the shop windows there was only the reflection of a drawn and haggard face. What a bride!

370

"O God," I said. I was miserably sorry for Sam.

Then I saw Paddy coming down the street.

Paddy, his face all wrinkled up with laughter, his eyes only a crease beneath his brow and his coarse curly hair tousled and so exactly like Paddy it couldn't be anybody else.

"Hallo, My-adora," he said, his voice soft, gentle and very Irish.

"Paddy," I said accusingly. "You haven't answered the invitation to my wedding. Aren't you coming?"

"Nope. Neither'o Paul. We're going to get drunk. We're starting to-day."

He put out his finger and touched my mouth. His eyes were looking into mine. Neither of us cared that the population of Perth was slowly flowing past us.

"Oh, that troubled mouth . . .!"

He took both my hands and bending his elbows folded my hands against his chest. His dear Irish face was close to mine and his soft Irish voice, tender as music, in my ears.

"I see your troubled eyes, Theodora. I see the fright is on you. Don't do it, darrlin'!"

"No power on earth will stop me, Paddy."

"But why? In God's name why?"

"I don't know. I just don't know."

"Do you love him?"

"I don't know. I just know I'm marrying him . . . that nobody, nothing could stop me."

"There must be a reason."

"There is . . . somewhere. I just don't know what it is. Paddy dear, please don't make me cry."

"Here's Paul," said Paddy looking over my shoulder.

"Well, well, well!" said Paul expansively. "What's this? Love scene in Hay Street? Not done on wedding-eve you know. Specially with a strange man."

"Fat lot you care," I said. "You're not even coming to my wedding."

"Not on your life," said Paul slapping his chest. "Absolutely frightful thing to go to a successor's wedding. Besides we've things of great moment to do."

"Don't boast," I said. "I know it's nothing but a drunk-up with Paddy."

"Isn't that important?" said Paul surprised, and his eyebrows arched over his forehead.

"Come and let's start," said Paddy linking his arm in mine.

"Not for me," I said. "My stomach wouldn't stand it."

"Just one wee drink with us, Theodora," he pleaded.

Paul took my other arm and they marched me, three-musketeer fashion, down the street to the pub.

We bent our heads together. Paddy's curls, Paul's golden sheen, and mine . . . dark, tousled, unset . . . were almost crown to crown like three conspirators.

"Water," I said weakly to the steward.

"Water be damned!" said Paul. "Bring her lemonade with a dash of port in it." For a moment he looked at me with understanding. "That won't hurt your stomach," he said gently, and then added. "Don't be frightened, Theodora. You can't trample in Sam's garden you know. He won't let you."

"You know what?" said Paddy. "Man I met on the train asked me why I was born in Dublin!"

"What's the answer anyway?" said Paul. "I've often wondered myself."

"Why!" said Paddy surprised. "Why! To be near my mother, of course."

His eyes creased up and the wheezy hilarious laughter began to rattle in his throat. We laughed eagerly, hungrily, afraid that laughter would leave us for ever. We three who had laughed among the reeds of the river . . . and who had all loved one another!

Paddy picked up my hand and held it against his cheek.

"My-adora. Don't do it, darrlin'. Don't do it!"

"Nothin'll stop me," I said fixedly.

"What about your own stream of blondes?" said Paul, supercilious. "You've been on the point of getting married three times this year, and to three different persons."

"Shut up, Paul," said Paddy. "I'm talking fatherly to Theodora."

He pleaded with me.

"It's all wrong, darrlin'. You don't belong. Nothing against Sam. Sam's absolutely all right. Plaster anyone against the wall who says different. But not for you, My-adora. Why you belong on the mountain tops . . . in the storm of the wind. That's you, Theodora. But shut up in a library? My God, Theodora!"

Paul slapped him on the back.

"Absolutely right, Paddy," he said.

"Listen, you two," I said. "You've had

your say in my life. And what you said wasn't any good. Now you can shut up. To-morrow, in sha Allah, I'm going to marry Sam. And no power on earth can stop me."

Paddy bowed his head, then he looked up and we stared at one another. He wagged his finger under my nose.

"Why are you looking at me like that, Theodora?"

"I can't see very well," I said. "I don't like wearing my glasses because I look school-marmish."

"School-marmish? Good heavens," said Paul. He bit his fingernail and stared at me, then leant over the table.

"Theodora, for the good of your soul, and the sake of all your friends, put on those glasses!"

I shook my head.

"I'll stay the way I am—a bit long-sighted that's all."

Dear crazy Irish Paddy! As he looked at me now his eyes were full of tender care. Between us there was the understanding of one "stinking Irishman" for another. We had a common and terrible heredity—one that sometimes trails clanking chains and sometimes clouds of glory.

His voice was so soft I could hardly hear it and I had to bend my head close to his.

"My-adora," he said gently. "Good-bye!"

"Good-bye, darling," I said. "Good-bye to youth and madness; good-bye to Paddy; good-bye to all that!"

We went out of the pub and they ushered me, the two of them, triumphantly to the hairdresser.

"So long, Theodora, think of us when you're at the altar. We'll be under the counter."

"Good-bye, Paul. Good-bye, Paddy." Both of them charming and lovable; doomed to be loved!

They went away, their shoulders back, their hands in their pockets and the will to drunkenness resolute in their bearing. They did not turn their heads.

The next day, trailing white lace and a shower of flowers, I went to the church.

It seemed to me when I left "Forty-five" on the arm of an old family friend that I left it a stranger and set out strangely on a strange way. I was tired and frightened. I had extended my nervous resilience beyond endurance. How was I to get through this awful ceremony?

I did not hear the prayers. I was suddenly aware of standing beside Sam at that moment in life when a girl gives herself, her body, soul and pride, into the hands of a man. She gives herself away, a parcel of white lace and flowers tied up with ribbon and orange blossom. And sometimes, like Theodora, she does not know what she is doing until the moment is over.

I looked blindly towards Sam and through the mist of my fright I saw the calmness of his face. His arm took my arm and I felt its strength.

It was rather beautiful and very safe. I could hear Sam's voice, quiet, grave and full of confidence. What angel had led me hither?

On that lovely spring morning I brought my head down out of the clouds and I saw that the sun was shining through the cherry blossom and shining on the earth. There was no rainbow and the only gold was a little band on my finger.

Perhaps in the ordinariness of home and hearth and husband I would come across another kind of rainbow. At the moment, in the strength of Sam's arm, I felt I had come home.

When I came out of the church it seemed that I had come out into the sunlight of living.

If there was the shadow of a short dark man in the church I did not know.

THE END

If you would like to know more about the
ULVERSCROFT FOUNDATION,
and how you can help to further its work,
please write for details to:

THE ULVERSCROFT FOUNDATION
The Green, Bradgate Road
Anstey
Leicestershire
England